THE
COURT-MARTIAL
OF
COMMODORE PERRY

OLIVER H. PERRY

From a portrait, after John Wesley Jarvis,
in the Redwood Library, Newport, R. I.

THE COURT-MARTIAL OF COMMODORE PERRY

by *JAMES A. RHODES*
and *DEAN JAUCHIUS*

THE **BOBBS-MERRILL** COMPANY, INC.
A SUBSIDIARY OF HOWARD W. SAMS & CO., INC.
Publishers · INDIANAPOLIS · NEW YORK

BOOKS BY

JAMES A. RHODES AND DEAN JAUCHIUS

The Trial of Mary Todd Lincoln

Johnny Shiloh

✳

BOOKS BY JAMES A. RHODES

Teen-Age Hall of Fame

✳

Appreciation is hereby extended to Culver Pictures, Inc.,
New York 16, New York, for use of the pictures in this book.

First Edition

Library of Congress Catalog Card Number: 61-7897

*This book is dedicated
to the memory of
OLIVER HAZARD PERRY,
a gallant and dedicated American
whose example, we sincerely hope,
will ever live in the hearts
of all Americans.*

✴

AUTHORS' NOTE

In his travels through the pages of history the modern writer often encounters a discordant note. It appeared to the authors of this book that in discovering the little-known facts of the Perry court-martial there was strong circumstantial evidence that a foul conspiracy had been at work against the illustrious Commodore during his naval career. The presentation of such a conspiracy as the heart of this book, although based on a circumstantial framework of fact, is supported by an intuition kept to its course by logic, and definitely seems to be in keeping with the tradition of Perry's career and his place in American history. As to the problem of reconstructing historical dialogue, we ask the reader to judge us on intent rather than on documentation.

We have made use of the author's license but we trust we have used it with the historian's conscience. We hope we have presented to the reader a plausible account of the situation which harassed Oliver Hazard Perry, and of how his conduct in battle was more than substantiated in the heroism of his private and professional life.

JAMES A. RHODES
DEAN JAUCHIUS

THE
COURT-MARTIAL
OF
COMMODORE PERRY

CHAPTER 1

DURING the maddeningly long winter journey, as he lurched and skidded by sleigh toward Lake Erie, Oliver Hazard Perry felt both excited and depressed.

Although he would not be twenty-eight for about six months, he prided himself in his family's long military tradition, his own ten years of naval duty, and his own readiness for any assignment. The one he had drawn did not quite live up to his expectations. He was *sleighing* to the command of a little unbuilt squadron on an island lake in the wilderness.

But he was going to see action—perhaps important action—at last! For a long time, while Stephen Decatur and the others had been teaching the British Navy how to fight, he had remained miserably shorebound.

Wryly, Oliver remembered one command: he had directed the inoffensive little gunboat flotilla that protected Newport, engaging them in sham battles, swallowing his impatience by immersing himself in gunnery and naval tactics. He was ready, able, eager to fight, but letter after letter begging for a sea command had been rejected by his superiors.

It was almost as though someone in a high place did not like him. He had asked for the *Hornet* and didn't get her. He had lost the *Argus*, too. In desperation, he had appealed to Commodore Isaac Chauncey, and Chauncey gave him this bone. By God, he'd make the most of it!

Approaching a wooden bridge, the horses whinnied nervously, breaking the train of his thought. He turned to the boy beside him.

James Alexander Perry was only twelve. He had a small boy's runny nose.

"Cold, mister?" Oliver asked.

"No. No, sir," James said quickly. He wiped his nose on his sleeve. "Just a little cramped, sir."

Oliver nodded. "Aye. So am I. Almost five weeks of this miserable sleighing. We'll be there in a few days now, mister."

The boy looked miserable, and Oliver caught the glint of tears in his eyes. "Wipe your face, mister," he said brusquely. "You've got snow in your eyes."

Although they were brothers, there was proper military formality between the commander and the shivering child. But Oliver now felt a quick protective ache. Why, the shaver must be homesick, he thought.

"I was just your age, mister," he went on more gently, "when Father went to see the *General Greene* properly built. I went with him."

The tears welled up as James thought of his mother, so far away in Rhode Island.

The man bridled. "Mister, if you're a Perry, you're a Navy man! And if you're a Navy man, you go where you are sent!" His voice suddenly softened. "I miss Mother and Father too. And Elna. Some day, mister, when you're older, you'll realize how hard it is to leave a wife."

"Yes, sir," the boy said, wiping his nose again. "I'm not crying. It's that snow that keeps blowing in my face."

"Sure, mister, sure. You're a Perry. Father and five of us Navy men, and two of your sisters married to Navy men. Just remember that."

It *was* a grand, strange fighting heritage. Oliver started to tell the boy more, then thought better of it. James was engaged in his first important battle—let him fight it privately.

The man turned the events of the past few days over in his mind. Twenty-four hours after receiving Chauncey's orders, he had sent a detachment of fifty men to Erie. Five days later, on Washington's Birthday, he and James had begun the journey. No time lost there. Fifty carpenters coming from Philadelphia. Had they arrived? What were Brown and Dobbins doing? Good men. He trusted them, but—— He had to see for himself.

The sleigh pulled off the road alongside a small, forlorn log tavern. "What's this, driver?" Oliver demanded. "Surely we can get further before nightfall."

"Sorry, Commander." The driver touched his hat. "Horses plain tuckered by those drifts back by the bridge. If we can't get a change, we'll have to rest them, or they'll founder on us."

Oliver gestured impatiently. "Do what you can! If this war ends while Oliver Hazard Perry is off sleighing, I'll have somebody's hide!"

Finally the journey was ended. At Presque Isle, Oliver jumped stiffly from the sleigh, almost falling awkwardly. James was out with the agility of a boy, standing a respectful pace to the rear, as Sailing Master Dan Dobbins and Shipwright Noah Brown greeted them.

"Quite a way to take over a naval command—from a sleigh," Oliver said cheerfully. "Now, gentlemen, let us waste no time."

"Begging your pardon, sir," Dobbins said soberly, "but it's quite a command."

"What do you mean, sir?"

Dobbins glanced toward Brown, the sturdy, patient shipwright who had come from New York to build the wilderness squadron.

"The keels of two twenty-gun brigs and three gunboats have been laid," Brown reported. "The rest to be done with wood from this virgin forest." He paused. "I don't like working green wood, sir."

"Are your carpenters complaining?"

"Most haven't yet arrived. They've left Philadelphia, but you know what winter travel is, sir. Latest word we got is that the trip is taking five weeks, like your own."

Oliver conquered the dismay before it reached his face.

"Now, Dan," he said, turning to his sailing master, "I'll be needing a lot from you, like a master in strange waters depending on a pilot. You're a Great Lakes navigator, and you've been a trader through this howling wilderness. What say you?"

"No rope, no canvas, and no iron for gun mounts, braces, chains and anchors," Dan said. "Not even a plan for protecting the ships on the stocks."

Indignation suddenly blazed in his dry voice. "What do they expect you to do, sir! *Talk* the enemy into surrender?"

"There will be a plan, sir," Oliver reassured him. "And fast. We must first protect what we have. And after that, if I have to scrounge the countryside myself with this boy here, there'll be rope, canvas and iron."

Oliver spoke with a much greater confidence than he felt. The thought crossed his mind—but he quickly dismissed it—that Commodore Chauncey had not conferred a favor on him. Perhaps, considering the petty intrigues and jealousies that seemed to be building as fast as the new little American Navy, there had been a deeper motive in letting him undertake this formidable task. He flushed at his own suspicion.

"Another thing, sir," Dan Dobbins continued dolefully. "Lieutenant Elliott says it can't be done."

"What can't be done before it's tried?" Oliver demanded. He spoke

13

more irritably than he intended. Actually, Chauncey's first choice for the Erie assignment had been Elliott. But he hadn't wanted the job. Oliver had gone over Chauncey's head then to get it, and he wondered whether the old man and Elliott resented it.

"What does Lieutenant Elliott feel cannot be done before it is tried?" he repeated.

"Says there ain't enough water on the bar to get them brigs into the lake," Dobbins explained. "As a matter of fact, he claims there ain't a harbor on all Lake Erie where a squadron can be built and fitted."

Oliver squared his shoulders. "I say, Mr. Dobbins, that we will finish these ships. We will build them and equip them and lift them over the bar. I say that it *can* be done, and it *will* be done."

Dobbins' face lighted. "I'm old enough to know a fighting man," he said, more cheerfully. "You just give the orders, commander, and I'll do my part. So will the men. I promise."

"And you, Brown?" Oliver turned to the shipwright.

Brown pursed his lips, then judicially spat a dark stream of tobacco juice that stained the snow.

"Tain't the comforts of the East River here, sir," he rumbled. "But a good workman, like they say, don't complain of his tools. Get me them Philadelphia carpenters we hear such talk about. And get me them supplies."

"You'll get them, Brown."

"Then you'll have your little navy, sir. No *Constitutions*, mind you, but fast, well-bottomed ships. We want to win this war, too!"

"Thank you, gentlemen. I look forward to the day when we can show that Lieutenant Elliott was misinformed."

The forests rang to the choppings of Perry's axmen. Brown's carpenters, although they looked imploringly to heaven and swore voluminously at their woodland workyards, none the less hammered, nailed and planed with surprising speed. Begging, buying and commandeering, foraging details ranged the countryside for miles. The supplies of rope, canvas and iron fittings grew. When a piece was lacking, Brown diverted his men to other chores until the foragers returned from a successful mission.

Not with shipyard efficiency, but with a rough, steady make-do, Perry's squadron slowly came into being. Even the commander, although he was intermittently racked by an old fever and a nagging sense of responsibility, found himself occasionally smiling.

But at his snug headquarters, Commodore Isaac Chauncey fretfully shuffled papers, then stared in annoyance at Lieutenant Elliott.

"You made a bad mistake in strategy, Jesse."

"Sir?"

Chauncey tapped the papers before him. "These reports from Erie. I thought you shared my views that President Madison was ill-advised in approving the Lake Erie operation. That was why I suggested you for the command."

"But, sir, why should I be asked to take such a hazardous command?"

A Connecticut man who once had sailed John Jacob Astor's ships, Chauncey had much of the prudence and indirection that befits a merchantman—but not a fighting man. In a sea scrape, he liked to "edge away," as he put it, saving canvas and masts and cordage. In conversation he edged away, too. A subordinate had to divine what Chauncey was too wary to say openly.

"I thought you trusted me," he said reproachfully to Elliott. "I had thought that if you took the command, the situation would develop in such a way that we would prove the President wrong."

Elliott shifted, uneasy. Confound this old edge-awayer, he thought. Now he is almost telling me that I should have guessed his mind and done his bidding.

"Sir! I have never doubted the miswisdom of that operation. I have stated my opinion, frankly and openly, like a gentleman and an officer."

Chauncey's heavy-lidded eyes widened. He fixed Elliott with a glance that said more than words.

"Exactly, Lieutenant Elliott! Because you do talk so openly, because you distrusted my interest in your career, you forced me to appoint another man."

Elliott laughed harshly. "My opinion, sir, of Mr. Perry, both as an officer and as a person, dates back some years. I could not have been happier in the selection you made."

Chauncey stared. There was contempt in his voice. "If you would care to glance at these progress reports from Erie, I daresay your happiness will be short-lived."

Elliott's jaw dropped.

JESSE D. ELLIOTT

"Yes, Lieutenant, I indicated my disapproval of the operation. I felt that proper strategy is the collection of enough forces so that I could first win on Lake Ontario. You have, as you say, frankly—and, I might add, rashly—stated similar opinions. But Mr. Perry seems to be doing the impossible."

Elliott flushed. "If so, he must be stopped, sir! I have staked my reputation on the matter."

"Your language, again, is most imprudent, Lieutenant. One simply doesn't talk—or even think—of stopping an American expedition!"

"I'm sorry, sir. I just meant that something had to be done. Perry—and how I've hated him for years!—is making fools of both of us."

Chauncey made a soothing, almost benedictory gesture with his hand. "For you, Lieutenant, continue as you have, in character, to state your frank and gentlemanly objections. Words come easy to you."

Elliott was stung, but he held his temper. His face clouding, he skimmed the reports from Erie that Chauncey handed him. "More than words will be needed now," he said quietly.

Chauncey sighed heavily, but there seemed to be a look of amusement on his face.

"Supplies and men, Lieutenant! Always they are such a pressing, critical problem. Perry bothers me for more of both. But you know how little I have to spare."

"Oh, indeed, sir!" This time Chauncey's meaning was plain, and Elliott felt a surge of relief. The old man was just going to starve that popinjay out in the wilderness. He laughed, a little too loudly.

"Mr. Elliott! The failure of an American squadron—anywhere—is no laughing matter. I will do all that I can."

Chauncey paused. Again the heavy-lidded eyes opened wide, and there seemed to be another meaning as he repeated, "I will do all that I can. But I may fail."

He's edging away again, Elliott thought. He's trying to tell me that maybe he can't stop Perry.

"And if I fail, Mr. Elliott, I may require your services in a more strenuous way than talk. That is all, sir."

For a brief moment, sincere anger flashed in those heavy eyes. "Why, sir, didn't you take that command in the first place! Good day!"

Alternating between praising the work gangs and berating them as impossible landlubbers, Perry watched every detail, personally inven-

BUILDING THE FLEET ON LAKE ERIE

toried his slim supply of canvas, exhorted and threatened the foragers. Somehow, despite the unrelenting pressure that he applied, the men did not resent him. Even the civilian crews recognized the passion that drove him, and they felt proud, even grateful, to be hammering for this fighting American patriot.

Though the job before him was formidable, Perry was heartened by one thing. Presque Isle was the only place on the lakes where the enemy could not seriously molest him as his command lay landbound, building their ships.

His eyes darted restlessly as he studied the large bay, the low, sandy peninsula which nearly surrounded it, and the narrow entrance channel, shallow and winding. In good water, with an inshore breeze to pile it higher, the depth of water in the channel was maybe six feet, no more. Perhaps, as Elliott had feared, Perry could not get out, but neither could the British sail through the narrows and cross the bar to challenge his unmanned squadron.

An attack from the lake would be feasible only if men were landed to advance on Presque Isle. And, just to checkmate such an operation, General Harrison had sent him 500 militiamen. The sandbank, probably a mile wide, ran in a southeast direction to the shore of the mainland, and between the sands and the militia, he was safely protected.

But the militia couldn't lift his landlocked brigs out into the lake, and the sandbar could hold them back. It was going to be quite a task, he admitted privately, to move his squadron out into action.

So quietly that Perry started, Sam Hambleton came alongside him. Sam, a Navy purser, was an old and very special friend and did not feel it necessary to clear his throat respectfully when approaching the commander.

"Sorry, sir," he apologized. "Didn't mean to startle you. I was just wondering if you were studying on the same problem that keeps bothering me inside. When we're built and ready, how in the world will we get to lake water?"

"Sam, when you were a boy, did you listen to your father's stories?"

"Not always," Sam admitted. He smiled. "The old man talked a lot, and it got pretty tiresome sometimes."

"You should have listened, Sam, you really should have. Now I listened to my father, and I learned a lot. Remember, he was a privateer in the Revolution. He served on the *Mifflin*, too, and aboard the *Trumbull* when she met the *Watt*. He was captured and then escaped from that stinking Jersey prison ship and was captured again and imprisoned in Ireland. The old man, you can imagine, had a lot of sea yarns."

"Even the crazy Irish can't sail over sand," Sam grumbled.

"You interrupt me, Sam. It wasn't the Irish I was leading up to. It's the Dutch."

"That fever ain't acting up again, is it, sir?"

Perry laughed. "No, Sam, but seeing as you seem to distrust my mental facilities, I'll drop the subject. I will just tell you that from the Dutch, through my father, I know how to sail over sand."

"Your face looks a little flushed. You've been working steady, day and night, most nigh to two months now. Get some rest, sir."

"Sam, you're a priceless man! You're the only friend I have who can call me lightheaded to my face, and somehow I don't mind it at all. Now kindly find Noah Brown and bring him here. Make it very casual. I don't want the men to know what I have in mind."

With a troubled side glance at Perry, Hambleton left. He returned ten minutes later with the stocky shipwright. "Thank you, Sam. Now if you will just allow me to talk privately to Noah for a few minutes, I'll take my awful medicine and lie down. Agreed?"

"All right, sir, I'll move along a bit."

As soon as Sam was out of earshot, Perry turned to Brown. "They're good brigs you're building, Noah, both of them."

"Aye, sir. It's coming better than I'd hoped. A lot of sweat and backache has gone into them. One hundred and forty-one feet long and thirty-foot beams." There was a workman's pride in his voice. "And four hundred and eighty tons, sir. Not Indian canoes, you might say."

"And don't forget, Noah, pierced for twenty guns, ten to a broadside. They have sting, man, sting! But now I need something special from you. Can you build me some scows?"

Brown's weathered, rough face clouded angrily. "Begging your pardon, sir. We're doing the best with what we've got, and we ain't building any scows, as you see fit to call them."

"Come, now, Noah, you know me better than that. I never use cheap talk, and why should I, to you? You're an artist, Noah. No, I meant I really need some scows, or long floats like scows. I have a very special reason."

From his jacket Perry extracted a paper on which he had penciled a rough sketch of a long, ungainly, flat-topped barge, together with approximate dimensions. "You can keep this, Noah, but first let me go over it with you in detail. We're getting to the point where there just can't be any mistakes."

For fifteen minutes, as Sam Hambleton paced back and forth a dozen feet away, Perry and the shipwright talked. Then, carefully folding the paper in his big, gnarled hands, Brown asked, "Just one more question, commander. What kind of naval use might these things have?"

Perry shook his head. "Noah, I trust you implicitly, as I trust Sam. But a secret shared is a secret lost. We have occasional 'visitors' here whom I strongly suspect keep the enemy fully posted on our progress.

"Now, if one workman knew the why of it and blabbed, we'd lose all the advantage of surprise."

"If there's spies about, they'll see us building them," Noah protested.

"Let them," Perry said grimly. "It will give the British something to wonder about."

Brown left, rejoining Sam Hambleton. Perry, alone, smiled as a puff of wind carried Sam's words back to him. "Noah, I'm worried about him. Didn't he seem a little lightheaded to you from the fever?"

CHAPTER 2

As FAR back as he could remember, Oliver Hazard Perry had taken it as a simple, childish act of faith that someday he would be a fighting man.

There was the salty, dominating example of his father, Christopher, a Rhode Islander and, so strangely, descendant of Quakers. And yet not so strange perhaps. The Perrys had been militant Quakers. The first one in the country, Edmund, had been heavily fined for pamphleteering against the authorities of Plymouth Colony, and his son had joined the courageous protestants in the land that was to become Rhode Island. One way or another the Perrys were fighters.

After his Revolutionary adventures, Oliver's father had remained at sea, both as a post-captain of the infant Navy and as a merchantman voyaging to the East Indies. He was in his fifties now but still openly unmellowed in his opinion of the British.

Through his mother, Sarah Alexander, Oliver knew that there was even more fighting blood. During the troubled 1600's in Scotland, Sarah's grandfather had been an officer in the Scottish Army, one of the many who had to flee to Northern Ireland. Sarah, who had been orphaned as a young girl, grew up in an uncle's home in Ireland.

She had first met Christopher Perry when he was imprisoned in Ireland during the Revolution, and later he had been mate on the sailing vessel that carried her to New York. When they arrived, they were married in the home of the great Dr. Benjamin Rush.

Oliver smiled faintly as he remembered how he had teased Sam Hambleton about listening respectfully to one's father. In his own case he might as well have added mother, for Sarah was really the firebrand of the family.

Very properly, she had guided Perry's reading to the Bible, Shakespeare, Addison and Plutarch's *Lives*, and she had seen to it that he received polish, as well as education, under the tutelage of the stern Mr. Frazier in Newport. But she had never tired telling her five boys, and the three girls too, of their fighting tradition.

Oliver was following in that tradition. Already he had served aboard the *Adams, Constellation* and the *Constitution,* and seen action twice in the Tripolitan War. He had commanded the schooner *Revenge* and though she was wrecked off Watch Hill, Rhode Island, the court of inquiry had exonerated him.

And it was the same with the others: Raymond H. J., Matthew Calbraith, Nathaniel Hazard and little James Alexander here with him at Presque Isle. All Navy men. Why, even two of his three sisters, Anna Marie and Jane, were married to Navy men—a captain and a surgeon! He must tell it all again to James. The boy looked peaked and still a bit homesick.

May 24, 1813

Nervously, reproaching himself for the unseemly excitement, Oliver waited for the last of Noah Brown's carpenters to finish their mysterious puttering and clamber off the brig. She was ready for her launching, and the strongest of the work gangs stood ready with sledges to knock the restraining timbers from the ways.

"Noah, can't those men hurry!"

Noah chewed, spat and regretfully removed his tobacco cud. Then, with a roar that would have done honor to a quarter-deck, he assured his landlubbers that they would become sailors in just five minutes unless they finished their blasted hammering.

There was a frenzy of activity, men slid down the ropes and Noah turned to Perry. "It is your privilege, sir, to give the word." Quietly, Perry passed the order, and the sledges slammed against the blocks.

With strange creakings and groanings, the vessel stirred. For an awful moment she seemed to teeter, then shot like an arrow toward the water. Fur caps, hammers, saws flew into the air.

"There she goes! Damn the British! Hurrah for the American Navy!"

The strength suddenly drained out of Perry, and he lurched against Sam Hambleton. "Sorry, Sam, I lost my balance."

"You should rest, sir. Down a scupperful of grog, climb into the hammock and have at it at full sail."

"I will now, Sam. I promise I will."

Slowly Perry picked his way through the cheering mob to his quarters. Hannibal, his big Negro body servant, looked at him worriedly. "They's a message just arrived from Commodore Chauncey, suh."

Perry shook his head as though he could shake the fatigue out of his mind. "Let me have it, Hannibal, before I turn in."

With proper Navy courtesy, Perry read, Commodore Chauncey had the honor to report an imminent campaign against Fort George and to offer Perry the command of 500 seamen and marines—if he could join him forthwith.

"Hannibal!" Perry shouted. "I can't waste time sleeping. Get me some grub and prepare my things. I must join Commodore Chauncey."

Just then Sam Hambleton appeared, exhibiting an elaborate nonchalance. "Just passing by," he said. "Need anything."

"I've no time for sleep! I'm joining Chauncey as soon as possible."

"Joining Chauncey! What for? You've got Presque Isle and he's got Lake Ontario."

"But, Sam, sounds as though he really wants me on hand. He's going to hit Fort George, the British outpost on the Niagara. That's important."

"You mean it's important to the Army and to Chauncey. Sir, your job is here. You've supervised everything from the casting of the guns at Georgetown to the rigging and sailmaking."

"Sam, quit worrying! I've been around the Horn, you know. I can take care of myself."

"Well, maybe if you have to be a stubborn American Yankee Doodle Dandy patriot, you'll be strong enough in a day or two."

"I leave tonight, Sam."

"Tonight! Why, you're light-headed again from the fever. I best call Doc Parsons."

"Sam, once and for all, I leave tonight. Now get out!"

It was a raw night and, as the open, four-oared boat left Presque Isle, Perry twisted in his greatcoat, trying to get comfortable. But, fighting squalls and headwinds, the light craft pitched and rolled maddeningly. Perry gave up all hope of sleep.

"Lay on the oars," he encouraged his sodden crew. "I promise you two things. Make Buffalo by tomorrow evening, and you can have a full night's sleep. After that, if you've got the belly for it, there'll be action!"

They reached Buffalo in time for the blessed, dry night's sleep ashore and then early next morning, Perry briefed them on the ticklish part of the job.

"Don't slap oars, don't talk," he said bluntly. "We're going down the Niagara under the muzzles of British muskets. I propose to land above the rapids—intact, if possible."

Furtively, under the cover of a violent rainstorm, the little boat crept down the middle of the river, the men responding slowly and painstakingly to Perry's whispered commands. Several times he held his breath, almost sure that the British had seen them and would challenge or open fire. But each time a sudden gusty sheet of rain enveloped them and they passed by safely.

"Ship oars!" Perry suddenly whispered. "Listen!"

From somewhere ahead the wind brought noises: a horse's whinny, the sudden jingle of a spur, a sergeant's command, startlingly clear. "It's *our* army," Perry said. "It must be! Full on the oars."

The boat grated ashore some distance from the encampment, and the men threw themselves down on the beach in relief. "Ten minutes' rest," Perry said. "Then we present ourselves in proper military order."

As he called them to attention, a sailor came forward somewhat sheepishly, leading a sway-backed old mare, without saddle and with a makeshift rope bridle.

"Best I could scrounge, sir," he said apologetically. "But at least the commander can ride."

Laughing, Perry clambered onto the nag. She neighed indignantly and sidestepped as she felt his wet clothing on her bare back. He yanked hard on the bridle to quiet her.

"Fall in!" he commanded. "March!"

What a spectacle, he thought, as he led his men to meet the Army.

A pretty craft, though Perry knew she had been raced to construction in only nine weeks, Chauncey's corvette *Madison* lay off the beach encampment. After making the proper amenities to the Army, Perry was rowed out to her on the night of the twenty-sixth. It was precisely two nights after he had received the commodore's message. Chauncey's eyes widened in astonishment as Perry stooped to enter the little cabin.

He didn't think that I would make it, Perry thought with some satisfaction. He just didn't think it could be done. Then why did he send for me at all?

Quickly Chauncey masked his surprise. "I knew I could depend on you, Oliver. Knew you wouldn't want to miss a good show, too. Now let me outline the operation and get your always invaluable advice."

But in Chauncey's crabbed, edging-away manner, there were other things on his mind than the engagement immediately ahead.

"I'm sorry about the supply situation, Oliver. Wanted to explain it firsthand. I simply can't spare what you need. I fear that leaves us with only one thing to do."

"And what is that, sir?" Perry asked grimly.

"I don't like to say this, Oliver, but I hope you will take it in the fatherly spirit that is intended. You are young, impatient. Perhaps, in your position, you couldn't be expected to have the over-all strategic picture."

God, thought Perry, how he tacks about!

"For your own sake, Oliver, don't attempt precipitate action. When, as and if, you will get the men and supplies."

The meaning was clear. Chauncey was telling him to wait patiently like a good boy. Perry bridled at the implied threat in the phrase "for your own sake."

Maybe it was fatigue, maybe it was just that Chauncey was not Perry's kind of Navy man. Either way, Perry decided, there might as well be a showdown.

"Begging your pardon, sir, I wish to differ. Action at the earliest date is imperative. I have taken the liberty of expressing these views to Washington, a copy of which communication I have brought for you."

For a second, naked hate flashed in Chauncey's eyes, then the heavy lids partially closed. He accepted the envelope that Perry proferred him and stuffed it in his coat without looking at it, as though the matter were unimportant.

"Perhaps this will prove to have been unwise on your part, Oliver," he said mildly. "I like to think that you have a long and useful career ahead of you."

He let the sentence dangle.

"The letter has already been dispatched," Perry said shortly. "Washington must decide whether I get what I need."

Chauncey sighed. "So be it. Now, time is getting short. We'd best get to the matter at hand."

At least for the immediate operation, he went on, supplies, men and small boats were no problem. The water, as Perry must have seen for himself, was covered by hundreds of boats loaded to the gunwales with soldiers, horses and artillery pieces.

But the landing was going to be bloody unless the Americans could enfilade the fort. Chauncey looked inquiringly at his subordinate.

"Perhaps we can anchor the *Ontario* and the *Asp* in positions so that their fire will enfilade," Perry suggested.

"Don't see how we can get them up that current," Chauncey objected. "The *Niagara* runs at least five knots there, even seven in some places."

"Drag them through. Give me fifty seamen and two hundred soldiers, and I can do it!"

"Never heard of such a thing!" Chauncey said. "Whatever gave you that fool idea?"

"La Salle." Perry's eyes twinkled as Chauncey wrinkled his forehead in bewilderment. "I read about the old boy doing it, Commodore. He put the first sailing vessel on the lakes, you know. That was clear back in 1679. If he could do it, we can."

"Impossible!"

"Nothing is impossible, sir. It only seems that way. Give me the chance."

Chauncey drummed his fingers on his tiny desk. "All right, Oliver. But you understand that this is entirely your responsibility."

During the night, straining at the long ropes, Perry's mixed gang of sailors and soldiers slowly worked the two schooners into position.

Then, the next morning, as the landing forces debarked upstream, the raking fire from the *Asp* and the *Ontario* kept the British from counterattacking, and the Americans quickly dug in their beachhead. From the nine-gun *Hamilton*, a steady hail of grape and canister poured on the British line. It was too much even for regulars, and the line broke.

As the British fell back, there was a frightening roar. The little schooners danced in the shock waves. The British had touched off their magazines. Fort George had fallen. The entire Niagara frontier would now be evacuated!

After the victory celebrations had ended, Perry reflected somewhat sourly to himself that, despite Chauncey's excellent support operation, there weren't any victories on the lake to be celebrated. Huddled in Buffalo Creek with an under-gunned fleet of five vessels, he wondered what his plan of action should be. Evasive, probably.

On his fingers he counted his gun power. Three twenty-four pounders on the *Caledonia*, two long thirty-two's on the *Somers*, one on the *Trippe*, one twenty-four pounder each on the *Tigress* and the *Ohio*. Only eight guns in all!

Why, the *Queen Charlotte* alone had 17 guns, not to mention 13 on the *Lady Prevost*, 10 on the *Hunter*, three on the *Little Belt*. Maybe —small consolation—the *Chippewa* carried only one. In all, 44 guns—

26

more than five times as many as he carried—and the British were roaring mad after losing Fort George.

It was early June now and on the lakes at that time of the year the seas were heavy. Perry wanted to beat for the protection of Presque Isle. He smelled the wind distastefully. For his course home, it looked like a headwind all the way. Yet, he thought, when in doubt, *act!* Better run for it than sit here and wait for disaster.

On the fourteenth the five little vessels cautiously poked their noses out of Buffalo Creek, then spread full canvas and tried to make a dash for it. Perry's fever was bothering him again, and he went below, leaving orders to be called at once if a strange sail were sighted.

In a ragged line the little fleet bobbed slowly toward home. Perry, moving restlessly in his bunk, tried to put himself to sleep by guessing at their progress. Finally, when he thought they must be nearing Presque Isle, he dropped off into a fitful slumber.

"Sail ahoy!"

The lookout's cry had him on deck in less than two minutes. Rubbing his eyes, he saw that his light ships were just safely clearing the harbor bar at Presque Isle. Racing toward them, but more than a gunshot away, was the towering *Queen Charlotte*.

Perry swore. "We'll have to run for it. She's got double the guns of all of us put together. Thank God, though, she can't get over the bar."

He motioned the deck officer. "Not too much sail, sir. Perhaps we should loaf a bit and at least pay our respects. Signal the others."

As the *Charlotte* rushed forward, there was the roar of the *Somers'* long thirty-two. Perry shook his head "Too soon. A miss."

A minute later he gave the order to fire, and the *Charlotte's* mizzen seemed to carry away. "That's all we can stand around for," he said unhappily, ordering the fleet in to safety.

Although the fever was still throbbing in his head, Perry felt a sudden pang of self-reproach as he stepped ashore. His brother James had been aboard the *Somers*, and he had forgotten all about him.

Quickly, Perry went to the *Somers*, hiding his relief when the twelve-year-old ran excitedly toward him. The boy had smelled his first gunpowder and liked it. Good!

"At least we saw a bit of action, eh mister?" he said casually.

"Aye, aye, sir!" Suddenly James looked as if he might break into tears. "But we missed them, sir. We missed!"

"You can't hit every time, lad. And experience on a long thirty-two is good for you. You learned something today."

"But we missed, sir!"

"Cheer up, lad. We took away the *Charlotte's* mizzen—or hit it, anyway."

Now James was smiling again. Perry smiled. "Now that you are a veteran, you will be writing all about it to Mother, I suppose?"

The boy blushed. "I had thought of it, sir, but not to brag. Just to tell the truth."

Perry laughed. "Only the truth, of course, like every sailor. But do one thing. Don't mention this bilious fever. Tell Mother that I am well and send my deepest love and affection. Otherwise, she will fret. Off now!"

As James scampered away, Perry slowly drew his sleeve across his sweating forehead. He felt burning hot one moment, clammy the next, but he knew he couldn't rest till he talked to Noah Brown. He found Brown down by the docks, bellowing orders to his Philadelphia carpenters.

"Oh, sir, begging your pardon, you look wretched," the old shipwright exclaimed. "I heard you had a little action just now and a big one up there at Fort George. Take an old man's advice and pace yourself."

"Gladly, Noah, as soon as you tell me one thing. The scows are coming along?"

"Almost finished, sir."

"And no gossip about what they're to be used for?"

"Even these Philadelphia experts are puzzled." Then, in hurt tones, Noah added, "As I am."

In spite of the fever, Perry smiled. "You'll be the first to find out, Noah. The very first."

CHAPTER 3

FINALLY both brigs were in the water, and Perry was trying to visualize how the square sails would look on the varnish-bright masts, how the flush-decked little furies would fly with a fresh, following breeze, canvas billowing and lee rails dropped low.

One, he had already decided, would be christened the *Niagara* in tribute to the successful attack on Fort George. Then a tragic message arrived from Secretary of the Navy William Jones, and he knew what he would *have* to name the second brig.

"This is bad," he said heavily to Sam Hambleton. "Jim Lawrence has been killed and the *Chesapeake* captured."

No doubt the hot-headed Lawrence had been foolhardy in accepting the challenge of the British frigate *Shannon* to the sea duel off Boston. The two frigates were well enough matched, but Lawrence had a raw, untrained crew, and the wily Captain Broke had supplied gun sights for the *Shannon* at his own expense.

The result was slaughter. Against the *Shannon's* total loss of only 85 men, 97 of Lawrence's men were killed outright during the June 1 engagement, and 99 more were wounded, 14 of them fatally.

"He was my friend," Perry said simply. He shook his head impatiently that Lawrence's impetuous gallantry had betrayed him into an uneven fight, capture and death.

"But he left us something precious, Sam. His last words. 'Don't give up the ship. Fight her till she sinks.'"

The two men were silent then, each wrapped in his own thoughts. Silently, they walked toward the harbor where the two brigs were anchored close together.

"Ships are strange, humanlike things, Sam," Perry said musingly. "These are built identically, and the *Niagara*, I have no doubt, is fast, as Noah Brown attests. Yet the *Lawrence*, I feel sure, for some reason is faster. She rides better, and her forefoot splits the waves in a way that pleases me. I think her planking and caulking are better, too."

He turned awkwardly toward his friend. "I'm not a mawkish man, Sam. But I want an appropriate battle flag, a field of blue, and big, bold, white letters that say, *Don't give up the ship*. Can you do it?"

"White muslin on blue silk would be fine," Sam said practically. "I can scrounge the material and find me a seamstress. Must be a Betsy Ross hereabouts. Swallow-tailed burgee was it that you had in mind?"

"No, Sam. I want a flag all of nine feet square with letters a foot high! When she flies from the main-royal masthead, I want the British to see those words."

From the British base at Amherstburg, Captain Robert Heriott Barclay, R.N., one-armed fighting son of a Scotch dominie, was writing again to Sir James Lucas Yeo, commander of all Lake Ontario.

Because of the poor condition of His Majesty's fleet on Lake Ontario, a senior captain, Mulcaster, had prudently declined the command, and Barclay now dismally realized that he should have perhaps done the same.

Patiently he reviewed his situation to Sir James. So long as the Americans remained unmolested, they would keep on building, and they had perhaps nine or ten vessels now to his six. He acknowledged, in all honesty, that he could scarcely ask for anything better than the new *Detroit*, 490 tons and 19 guns, and the scarred *Queen Charlotte*, a 400-tonner with 17 guns. The other four mounted 27 more, giving him enough to fight.

But men, he pleaded to Sir James, he needed men of the Royal Navy such as he had had the honor to command under Nelson at Trafalgar —not these raw Canadian boatmen, soldiers and *Indians!* Besides, provisions were running low at Amherstburg, and famine might force him into an engagement at an unpropitious moment.

Sir James courteously took Barclay's pleadings and warnings under advisement, and did nothing.

Lieutenant Thomas Holdup Stevens, commanding the little *Trippe*, was a proud sea cock, burning for action, and now his voice almost broke. "*When* do we go after them, sir?" he begged Perry.

"Aye, when indeed?" the commodore echoed. "There isn't enough time in all eternity, it seems, for Commodore Chauncey to send us men from Lake Ontario. Why doesn't the Secretary send me men and officers directly? This use of Chauncey as a way station is most unfortunate."

More than anything else, Perry restrained himself from voicing complaints to his subordinates. Bad for discipline and dignity, he thought. But young Stevens, so eager, so frustrated and puzzled, touched him. He reminded Perry of himself a few months ago when he feared he might ride out the war at mooring.

The anger rose in Perry's throat till he could almost taste it, and his voice trembled.

"It's a shame, sir! Chauncey has my Newport lads and *Constitution* gunners. Old-time tars with genuine queues sit at Sackett's Harbor, and we have no men.

"Aye, men glut Chauncey's ship, foc'sle and steerage! His *Pike*, with her single deck and only twenty-seven guns, can muster four hundred and seventy men. By heaven, they must ride each other's shoulders, stand on each others' hands aloft, foul the rigging!

"But no junior officers like you, no navigators, gunners, boatswains or marines have come to Erie. It is a shame, sir."

As quickly as he had erupted, Perry abruptly brought himself under control. Shaken by the sudden outburst, young Stevens was staring at him open-mouthed.

"You may judge, sir, that I aspire for action as ardently as you," Perry said more quietly. "I would be greatly obliged if you would consider this a personal and confidential conversation."

"Oh, yes, sir!" Again young Stevens' voice almost cracked. "But, begging your pardon, sir, I'm glad you feel this way. I feel highly honored to be under your command."

"Enough talk for today," Perry said gruffly. "Best get back to the *Trippe* now."

From spies and the trickling of intelligence that came to him from Washington, Perry discovered with a certain dry amusement that he and Captain Barclay, R.N., had many things in common, and only the inscrutable fortunes of war demanded that each do his best to kill the other.

They had been born in the same year, Perry of partly Scot descent and Barclay one of the "Black Barclays." Like Perry, Captain Barclay had entered the Navy at the age of twelve. While Perry had been seeing active service along the United States Coast and off Tripoli, Barclay had been in action many times in European waters, losing his left arm from a swivel shot in an unsuccessful attack on a convoy. Yes, the parallel was close, Perry mused.

He was deep in thought when Sam Hambleton came up behind him. "Notice how politely I coughed this time? Don't look good for a commodore to be jumping like a startled deer. You're strained, man. Need rest. A shinplaster, not a thing more, for your thoughts. Brooding about Chauncey?"

"No, Sam, I was thinking about the man we've got to tangle canvas with someday."

"Barclay? I hear he was at Trafalgar with Nelson."

"Aye, he's one up on me there. That and the lost arm—which I don't envy him. But, anyhow, Trafalgar was another time and place, and Nelson is dead."

"Remember Jim Lawrence, Oliver. Never underestimate the enemy."

"Not for a minute, Sam. When we meet Barclay, we're in for a battle, never fear. But the spies tell me that he is fond of good food and wine and most especially of the ladies. His mind dwells more on other things than on Erie's water, sir."

"And why not?" Sam asked with his usual practicality. "He hasn't so much at stake. His homeland is far away from the tomahawk and scalping knife."

"Exactly, Sam! I pray for the men and a weather break of even gauge. Then our men will give these British a fight they can't understand. There is our advantage."

Sam glanced toward the lake. Casually he beckoned at six saucy British sails that danced mockingly just beyond gunshot, off the Erie Harbor bar.

"And there's Barclay's advantage," he said dryly. "You can't get out to him, but he beards you every day. Kind of annoying?"

Perry swore in frustration.

"Nine good ships, sound in plank and beam and all good sailers— and barely enough men to man one brig! Half of them down with lake fever, needing Doc Parsons day and night, and the Doc himself so weak that he needs two tars to help him walk. I——"

Abruptly he stopped. "Sam, I'm *not* going to blow my mainsail, the way I did with young Stevens."

"Do you think General Harrison understands our situation?" Sam asked.

"I've tried to keep him informed," Perry said tiredly. "He probably thinks I just don't want to tangle with the British. His messages fairly reek with impatience. So do Secretary Jones's."

"They probably suppose, naturally enough, that we're getting a fair share of the men sent to Sackett's Harbor," Sam said consolingly.

"It's a supposition that frustrates the temper out of me! If Barclay were neutralized, Harrison could move on Canada, force Proctor from Detroit and Malden, and recover Michigan."

It was the same, day after day, as they waited. The "bearding" of Perry had been continuing since July 1, and though ordinarily he deplored any waste of shot and powder, he began to worry about the men's morale.

Making an excuse to shake Sam Hambleton who, he knew, would try to mother-hen him out of the plan, Perry went to his quarters, ostensibly to rest. "Hannibal, I'm going to bed."

The big Negro, almost as much of a nuisance as Sam, grinned happily. "But you're to rouse me at six bells," Perry added.

The Negro's grin faded. "Three *ayem*, suh?"

"Yes. And before I doze off, have someone pay my respects to Lieutenant Stevens and ask him to kindly report to me."

When the officer arrived, Perry outlined his plan. Before dawn, he planned to have the *Tigress* with her twenty-four pounder and the *Somers*, which could unlimber two long thirty-two's, anchor fairly close to the bar.

"It's cat-and-mouse and probably a waste of ammunition," he grumbled. "But if we catch the right breeze, maybe we can singe their beards with a long shot or two."

Stevens' face fell. "And the *Trippe*, sir?"

"Well, I'll be cooked," Perry said innocently. "Did I forget you? The *Trippe*, sir, will lay alongside the *Somers*, and I propose to be aboard your sloop during our little party."

"Thank you, sir."

"No special thanks, Mr. Stevens. It is a small honor you have more than earned. I am mindful of your deeds on the Niagara frontier before joining me."

Stevens blushed uncomfortably.

"One of the leaders of a detachment that captured the enemy's artillery and of a scaling party that dislodged the grenadiers by burning their barracks?"

"Yes, sir."

"Wounded, weren't you, by a canister shot? And then, with a couple of other daft midshipmen and five seamen, crossed the Niagara in a leaky canoe?"

"It really didn't leak much, sir."

"How old are you, lieutenant?"

"Nineteen, sir, next George Washington's birthday."

Perry burst out laughing. "And this is only July, my *eighteen-year-old* fighting cock. Mark my words, Mr. Stevens, rein your impatience, and you'll go far in this Navy."

Well before dawn, the three vessels were in position, the *Somers* off the *Trippe's* larboard bow, the *Tigress* just astern. Punctually, the six British sail appeared just ahead of sunup.

"We could cross the bar after them," Stevens said hopefully.

"No, mister. The odds are two-to-one in ships and more than that in guns against us. We wait."

For hours the intruders executed lazy, tempting maneuvers just out of gun reach and, as the sun rose steadily, so did young Stevens' temper.

"Damn, sir! They beard us shamelessly, and we sit here like merchantmen. How long do we wait?"

"Mr. Stevens, your impatience is showing. Most of war is waiting, you will find. I must admit I find it trying to wait for men and supplies. But when the enemy forces the waiting, mister, I can outwait them. If I teach you nothing else, you'll be the better for this lesson."

Shortly before noon the breeze failed, and the big enemy vessels found themselves suddenly becalmed. "Now," Perry breathed. In position the lighter *Tigress, Somers* and *Trippe* moved close to the bar. The crews of all three watched as Perry's tall, commanding figure methodically studied the six motionless sails with his spyglass.

He stepped back, lowered the glass and turned to the gun captain. "Ready on the gun?" he asked quietly.

"Ready, sir," the petty officer said.

"Fire!" Perry spat the command.

A bare-chested fireman touched the smoldering match to the long gun's touchhole. Perry braced himself, feet widespread, and fitted the glass to his right eye again.

There was a sudden roar, and the little sloop shuddered and rocked as the big thirty-two pounder blasted stinging blue smoke over the sunny water. Perry grunted. A waterspout near the sails showed the *Trippe* had fired short.

"This next time, Mr. Stevens, we shall see a strike," Perry said.

Again he studied the distant targets, then nodded to the gun pointer.

"Raise her three notches, lad. Steady on the mount! Gunner, fire when ready. I'll watch splinters fly if this glass is good."

The rammer shoved home the powder wad and shot, then moved clear. "Ready on the gun!" he shouted.

"Ready on the gun!" echoed the gun captain. He waited for the sloop's deck to level with the horizon. "Fire!"

Again, the big gun's recoil made the *Trippe* skitter, and the blue smoke hung almost motionless in the still air.

One of the distant sails flickered, as though a sudden gust of wind had caught it, but there was no wind. Slowly the sail collapsed.

Cheering rose from the *Trippe's* deck. "Well done, lads," Stevens shouted, his voice high with excitement.

Perry grinned tolerantly. "We've struck the *Queen Charlotte*, Mr. Stevens. Her fore-and-aft sail sags. I'll wager there's splinters on her deck, and that canvas won't draw any more today."

Now, from just astern, the *Tigress'* twenty-four pounder thundered into action, and from off the *Trippe's* larboard bow, the two long thirty-two's of the *Somers* belched noise and smoke.

"We have a few Yankee gunners," Stevens cried delightedly. "We're singeing their beards."

A long British shot fell close to the *Somers*, showering her decks with spray. Then a second plowed a deepening furrow off the *Trippe's* starboard quarter. Perry moved to the rail.

"They shoot short and weak," he said contemptuously. "As if their powder were wet. Or maybe they have little heart for more than bearding."

Suddenly his nose caught the scent of land odors from the heavy forests, and he swore. A fresh breeze was rising, an offshore breeze that would give the enemy a following wind so they could bear up and make away swiftly.

"They'll run now," Perry said disgustedly. "This new commander has no belly for long-range dueling."

"They didn't touch a one of us, sir," Stevens reported triumphantly.

"And we barely nicked them, no more," Perry said. He watched the far sails, golden in the sunlight, slowly melting into the horizon.

Nervously he tugged at one sideburn. "Barclay wants to fight, if he can close in, and I want to fight, close or long range. But I wait for the Navy brass."

"Ahem!"

Perry turned. Sam Hambleton was grinning at him. "Oliver, I give you the advice you handed this sea cock a few bells ago. Patience, man!"

"You're right, as usual, Sam. Bring the small boat alongside. Let's get back to the *Lawrence* at Cascade Creek."

CHAPTER 4

Moodily Perry tilted his head to look through the black lacework of the *Lawrence's* shrouds. The sails were bent and furled, waiting only for the topmen to sheet them home. *Waiting.*

Right now, his spies told him, Barclay's new full-rigger, the *Detroit*, was almost completed. Pierced for 19 guns, they said—and probably long ones, Perry thought to himself. One hope gone. He couldn't possibly get into action now before the *Detroit* was ready.

But the stakes were greater than the fate of his little squadron. From the first he had visualized the lakes as the key to the whole battle for the Northwest Territory. With the enemy swept from Lake Erie, Malden, Detroit and Dearborn would become untenable for them.

Right now, General Harrison was butted up against Britain's Proctor in northern Ohio. Without a fleet to support him, Perry thought impatiently, Proctor would be no more than a broken spinnaker boom. And that he wanted to see more than anything else. Proctor had shamelessly egged on the savages. Tecumseh, the copper-skinned brute, was a *brigadier* in His Majesty's service, and the whole frontier was stained with fire and blood.

A tentative rapping interrupted him. "Come in," he said.

Sam Hambleton entered, carefully carrying a bundle.

Perry looked up. "You don't usually knock, Sam."

Sam grinned sheepishly. "A little package just arrived from Mrs. Stuart in Erie. I thought you might want to see it."

"You rascal! The battle flag? Of course I do!"

Sam unrolled the burgee, making sure it did not touch the deck: "Sam, it's beautiful! Bainbridge, Hull, Steve Decatur will make them remember Jim Lawrence. But so shall we, Sam! *So shall we!*"

"If we ever get the men," Sam amended in his usual down-to-earth fashion. "Can't fight ships without gunners, boarders, pikemen, sail trimmers, boatswains and marines, sir."

Perry frowned. "Careful, Sam. Chauncey is a Tripoli veteran. Both of us were there with Decatur. I find it hard to believe Chauncey would want us to *lose* here."

"Well, we can't win the Northwest Territory sitting on unmanned ships. The green wood in them will sprout in this fresh water if Chauncey doesn't move soon. He must know that."

Perry sighed. He rubbed the palms of both hands across his sweating face.

"You're tired!" Sam's voice showed concern. "It's that blasted fever again. You don't get enough sleep for the sail you carry, sir. Let me stop talking, and you get some rest."

"Aye, Sam," Perry admitted. "My head is whirling."

As Perry slept, once again the cautious old commodore and the erratic young Lieutenant Elliott, unwilling, mismatched partners in intrigue, were conferring together.

"You will be pleased to know, lieutenant," Chauncey announced in his crabwise manner, "that I am sending reinforcements to Lake Erie."

"You can't, sir!"

"I must, sir! Washington has forced my hand."

Quickly he recovered himself. "What I mean to say, lieutenant, is that following consultations, I volunteered to send what few men I could spare."

As he usually did when he was happy, he sighed heavily. "I fear, however, that these landsmen will prove of little help to poor Oliver."

Elliott grinned. In other words, the old man was saying, under pressure from Washington, he had given Perry support, but shabby, token support. Now just let Perry complain to Washington again!

Chauncey was staring at him in distaste. "It seems, lieutenant, that I often find your mirth ill-placed—and premature. This little detail is a 'first deposit.' More men, some ships, even you, must follow to Presque Isle."

"I, sir! Under the command of Mr. Perry? Never!"

Chauncey benignly raised his hand. "Oliver is one of our finest officers. Whether we like it or not, it appears that he may lead a major sea engagement there shortly. He is, however, perhaps somewhat rash, and that is why I want you at his side."

"Most ignominious, sir!"

Isaac Chauncey

As though he hadn't heard, Chauncey began reminiscing in a deprecatory way about a shameful naval incident six years earlier.

Without right (as his own government subsequently admitted), the commander of the fifty-gun British Leopard had laid alongside the thirty-eight-gun frigate Chesapeake and coolly demanded the surrender of "deserters."

Elliot stiffened as Chauncey's voice droned on. "Properly, Commodore James Barron refused, and the Leopard opened fire."

"Twenty-one of the crew fell, three of them fatally wounded," Elliott put in defensively.

Chauncey waved him to silence.

"A young lieutenant ran up from the galley with a live coal and fired one shot. But that was all. Commodore Barron then struck his colors and surrendered the 'deserters.' Do you remember?"

"I was there, sir," Elliott said in a strangled voice. "I was a middie under Barron."

"And some fighting cocks like Perry were loud in their scorn, and Barron was court-martialed and suspended without rank or pay for five years. Am I right, Mr. Elliott!"

"I've never forgiven the bastard Perry to this day, sir!"

"Your language is imprudent, Mr. Elliott. I trust that when and if you go into battle in your own ship under Mr. Perry, your actions will be more prudent. Much more prudent."

"I don't quite know what you mean, sir."

"You wouldn't, Elliott. Think what I have said. That Mr. Perry is rash, and will undoubtedly so conduct himself in battle. That you are to be prudent in battle. We must win, of course. Mr. Elliott. But how. That's the crux of it! How. Think upon it."

At the end of July, Chauncey's "first deposit," a ragtag detail of 60 men, more than half of them ill with dysentery, arrived at Lake Erie from Sackett's Harbor. As Perry distributed the newcomers among his own awkward recruits, he studied the strange assemblage: Chauncey's ailing castoffs, old men, boys, Negroes, crude backwoodsmen. These were supposed to be seamen?

Wryly Perry wondered what the fastidious, trimmed beards in

Washington would think of such a naval task force. Sailors wearing buckskins and carrying long, wicked-looking knives? Indeed!

But, whatever the elegant admirals might think, Perry now could muster 300 officers and men, and his ships now mounted a total of 54 guns. It was time to move!

"Noah," he said to his shipwright, "I promised you would be the first to know my little 'secret.' Those scowlike contraptions you built for me are called camels. With them we'll lift the two brigs over the bar."

"Never heard of the things," Noah said suspiciously.

"Probably not. They were developed in Holland. My father taught me how they are used.

"You pull the plugs and half-sink one camel on each side of the brig, and then put big timbers through the ship's portholes, fore and aft, resting them on the camels' decks. Then you pump the camels dry, and when they reach full float, presto! They lift the brig with them. Then you tow brig and camels across the bar."

"I'll be damned. I always did hear those Dutch were clever."

"God help us though, Noah, if the British surprise us! That's why I had to keep my plan secret. We'll start immediately after church tomorrow aboard the *Lawrence*."

From dawn to midmorning on that first Sunday in August, Perry posted extra lookouts. Monotonously they reported all was clear.

As he had hoped, the bearders were observing the Sabbath. But there was another annoying and, Perry thought testily, unnecessary interruption.

Immaculate in full-dress uniform, General Mead and his staff paid a courtesy call. Grumbling at the waste of good powder, Perry ordered the *Lawrence* to fire a salute, and then received his unexpected guests.

As a result, it was high noon by the time both brigs were sailed to the bar and anchored near the shallows. Along the banks a crowd of some two hundred countrymen gasped and cheered at the sight of the huge, square canvas sails, sheeted home for the first time during the brief run.

It must have been the salute for Mead that attracted them, he thought. But then his men had often fired before, practicing on timbers towed behind schooners, and no such crowds had appeared. No, word of the impending lifting operations had somehow spread through the countryside. His palms sweaty, Perry prayed that the grapevine had not extended to Barclay's quarter-deck.

With his glass, he studied the faces of his unwanted audience, feeling a twinge of pity. These were the haunted faces of backwoodsmen, to whom the big ships and the great white sails were an only hope and an only defense.

First, Perry ordered the *Lawrence's* guns removed and placed on the beach. Next, she was stripped of all other weighty equipment which could be moved. Then the large, scow-shaped camels were worked into position on each side.

While this was being accomplished to the accompaniment of grunts and curses, the smaller vessels, which needed no assistance in crossing the bar, stood out into the lake. Decks cleared for action, they maneuvered into battle line to protect the helpless *Lawrence*. A larger gunboat, its long thirty-two's at ready, lay off the flagship as an additional cover, and landsmen hauled the *Lawrence's* heavy carronades up the beach, arranging them in a shore battery to cover the channel.

Nervously pacing the deck, Perry supervised the lifting operations from his brig. By nightfall the *Lawrence* rode awkwardly on huge timbers thrust through her portholes onto the flat-bottomed scows. In his master's cabin, unable to accustom himself to the strange, swinging motion of his ship, Perry slept restlessly.

For three days and nights, that was the last sleep he got. The circles under his eyes darkening, he directed the pumping operations that lifted the *Lawrence* half out of water. Then came the exasperatingly slow maneuver of hand-towing the brig and its unwieldly supports toward the lake.

Behind him other crews were readying the *Niagara*, and as soon as the *Lawrence* cleared the bar, the tow gang of red-eyed, exhausted sailors and militiamen would have to go back for her.

Finally the *Lawrence* was lakeborne, and after giving orders that she be immediately readied for action, Perry groped his way to his bunk. He did not even remember falling asleep.

"Sail ho! Sail ho!"

The lookouts' cries roused Perry. He stumbled onto deck, swearing and rubbing his eyes. It must have been some hours. Behind, the tow gang was heaving desperately on long bowlines to work the helpless, suspended *Niagara* over the bar. Ahead, on the horizon, Perry made out the enemy sail.

Quickly the little *Ariel* weighed anchor and stood out toward the oncoming line—a snapping terrier. In the *Scorpion*, Sailing Master Steve Champlin followed, firing furiously at long range.

Despite the brave bluster, Barclay had the gun power to drive the small vessels to cover in minutes if he felt like it. His ships returned the fire briskly but, at least for the moment, maintained their distance.

In the tense moment, as Perry wondered whether he should attack in the hope of saving the *Niagara* or run for it to save what he had, Sam Hambleton maintained his usual calmness. Methodically he checked the contents of the larboard and starboard arms chests.

"She's ready, sir," he said, reporting all the muskets and cutlasses accounted for.

"Aye, Sam," Perry said grimly. "But not the *Niagara*. Pray that bluster will see us through."

CHAPTER 5

FIRING more for effect than accuracy, the little fleet managed to keep the British at a distance, and the tow gangs moved the *Niagara* slowly over the bar. The British glasses would catch her movement, but Perry prayed that they couldn't pick out the line of straining men.

Suddenly the enemy ships bore up and stood across the lake. "Thank God, Sam! They suppose the *Niagara* is across the bar and ready. Otherwise, they would have come in and destroyed us. It's an omen!"

"What do you mean?"

"Given a fair breeze, we'll weigh anchor in the morning if the *Niagara* can be readied overnight, and stand off in double column to Long Point. Harrison has sent another urgent message. We'll wait no longer!"

"So few men aboard, sir." Hambleton looked worried.

"Aye, Mr. Hambleton," Perry said almost gaily, his spirits lifting at the prospect of action. "The fewer to be hit."

In the morning following, a breeze blew steadily. Perry took his position before the binnacle, watching the helmsman and signal offi-

BATTLE OF LAKE ERIE

cer. As he kept the sails set for best advantage, he listened for the singing chant of men with sounding leads, the cry of the lookout, the roar of surf which would mean danger.

It was a quick, easy run, and they stood in close at Long Point, guns ready, looking for the enemy. Perry's glass raked the waters. "Damn! They're gone!" Again, he swept the point with his glass.

"No use, Sam," he said, frustration edging his voice. "They're probably at Malden now, riding safely at moorings in the shadows of the fort's guns. Probably picking up the new *Detroit*."

"We've beat along this coast far enough," Sam said unhappily.

"Aye, let's stand back to Erie."

Irritably Perry shouted the orders for return, and the squadron executed the turning maneuver gracefully. Anticipation gone, they loafed home under less than half of their canvas as Perry fretfully paced the *Lawrence's* deck.

The next two days, the squadron took on large quantities of provisions and stores for Harrison's army. As the last of the casks were lashed on deck, Hambleton ticked them off on the manifest, and turned to Perry. "Let's go ashore this evening, sir. Let's eat at the hotel for a change."

"Aye, Sam, the luxurious accommodations of Duncan's Erie Hotel it is then."

"It's not such a bad port as that, sir," Sam said defensively. Being purser, he had made it his business to develop friends ashore. "I've seen worse chow."

"You will see worse again, no doubt. And worse grog, too. But hardly, Mr. Hambleton, hardly."

The two friends had almost finished a supper that, as Sam had to admit, was tasteless, when they were interrupted at the hotel.

"Beg pardon, sir," said Midshipman Montgomery. He approached Perry's table and stood stiffly at attention.

"This message arrived a short time ago for the commodore."

Perry thanked the midshipman and dismissed him. Opening the packet, he slowly read the message, then studied it again, his eyes thoughtful.

"Mixed blessings, Sam. Several officers and eighty-nine men on their way!"

"Hoorah!"

"And might you guess who is bringing them?"

"Not Chauncey, by any chance?"

"No, Mr. Hambleton. It is Captain Jesse D. Elliott himself."

"I'm thankful for the men, sir," Sam said stiffly.

Two days later, the *Ariel*, which Perry had promptly dispatched toward Cattaraugus to pick up Elliott's party, returned with the sulky captain, two acting lieutenants, eight midshipmen, a mastermate, a clerk and 89 men.

Praise God, Perry thought, I've either irritated Chauncey or good Providence has moved him at last. Fondly he studied the smart detachment of queued Newport men. "There's a salt-and-and-sun-bleached look about them, Sam," he said happily. "There are *seamen*. Still not enough, but a good beginning."

Perry's meeting with Elliott was brief and courteously restrained on both sides. He assigned Elliott to the command of the *Niagara* and instructed him to distribute the new arrivals through the squadron. In turn, Elliott gave Perry a letter from Chauncey, saluted and left to begin his new duties.

Chauncey's letter clutched in his left hand, Perry was standing by the *Lawrence's* larboard rail, blankly staring over the lake when Hambleton approached him. With Sam were Perry's younger brother James and Hannibal.

"It's about Captain Elliott's division of the men, sir," Hambleton said worriedly. "He's taking the best of the lot and the most."

"For the *Niagara*?"

"Aye."

"I rather thought he might," Perry said tiredly.

"It's not fair, sir! The *Lawrence* will be bearing the brunt of the battle. We ought to at least have our rightful share."

Perry hesitated a moment. He didn't quite know how to break the news to them. In Chauncey's letter, the commodore had accused him of "intimating the necessity of a separate command"—in effect, intriguing to obtain command of the Erie Squadron. That made it a matter of honor between them, and Perry knew he had only one recourse.

"Captain Elliott," he said, "may find himself aboard the *Lawrence*, rather than the *Niagara*, and in command."

Hambleton looked dumbstruck, young James and Hannibal puzzled. Perry told them of Chauncey's charges and explained that, since he really had no other alternative, he had roughed out a letter of his own to be posted to Navy Secretary Jones.

"This is the same Chauncey who has not, until now, sent me a single officer of rank or experience," he said slowly. "Elliott is not enough, and the men who arrived with him are not enough. What is needed is some drastic action to emphasize our needs—it would be a service indeed to my successor."

"Successor!" Hambleton almost shouted. He sat heavily on a lashed-down cask as if the strength had drained from his legs.

Perry nodded and, extracting the rough of his letter to Jones from an inside pocket, began reading it.

"I am under the disagreeable necessity of requesting removal from this station. The enclosed copy of a letter from Commodore Chauncey will, I am satisfied, convince you that I can no longer serve under an officer who has been so totally regardless of my feelings. . . ."

Characteristically, once his protest had been dispatched to the Navy Secretary, Perry gave it no more thought. Until he should be relieved, he intended to keep worrying his squadron into readiness, even forcing a showdown fight with Barclay if he could find him. True, he mustered fewer than four hundred men, including Chauncey's replacements, and many of the men were down with the lake fever. He shrugged. He could wait no longer.

Maybe, he thought, when he made the run through the lake for Sandusky Bay to deliver Harrison's supplies, Old Tippecanoe might spare him some men. God, he said to himself, right now I'd settle for the rawest Army recruits!

Aboard the *Lawrence*, he called his commanders into a war council. Possibly, he warned, enroute to Harrison, they might encounter Barclay and, if so, Perry wanted to make a fight of it. Supported by the *Caledonia*, *Scorpion* and *Ariel*, his flagship would engage the massive new *Detroit*. In the *Niagara*, Elliott would engage the *Queen Charlotte*, while the *Somers*, *Porcupine*, *Tigress* and *Trippe* would take on the *Lady Prevost* and *Little Belt*.

"Understood?" he asked sharply.

There was a chorus of eager "Ayes!" except from Elliott. "And you, Captain Elliott?"

"Understood, of course, Commodore." The man's tone stopped just short of insolence, Perry thought.

In the event of separation of the vessels and an accidental meeting at night, Perry went on, each ship was to hoist one light and hail, the one to the windward answering first with "Jones" and the one farthest leeward responding, "Madison."

"Identification being so nicely settled," Captain Elliott said silkily, "what is the commodore's plan if the enemy approach for an attack while we are anchored?"

Perry was more nettled than he allowed to show on his face. Damn this man! Elliott was making it seem as though he had overlooked an important point.

"I am coming to that, if you please, Mr. Elliott. Two quick musket shots from the *Lawrence* will be the order for all vessels to cut cable and make sail. The flagship will show a light, and the others will form astern of her, beginning with the vessel farthest to the leeward. Three successive shots will be the signal to weigh anchor in the same succession."

"Thank you, sir." Elliott was still trying to make Perry appear guilty of omission. "I merely raised the point because it seemed most important, sir."

"It is," Perry said shortly. "Scarcely one a commodore might be expected to overlook."

At last!

Perry stood on the *Lawrence's* stern, watching Erie disappear gradually into the horizon behind him.

The squadron sailed in double column, the *Lawrence* on the starboard with the *Porcupine, Caledonia, Ohio* and *Ariel* trailing. On Perry's larboard, Elliott's *Niagara* led the *Trippe, Tigress, Somers* and *Scorpion.*

I'll never forget this happy day, Perry thought with a sigh. When Erie was finally lost aft, he felt suddenly as though all his troubles and despairs had vanished, too.

For five days, as they beat toward the headquarters of the Northwestern Army at Seneca on the banks of the Sandusky River, Perry watched eagerly for hostile sail. Strangely, none appeared, and when they arrived at Seneca, Perry felt let down.

But cider-drinking Old Tippecanoe, hardened by warfare with the Indians, stoically resigned in the knowledge that he enjoyed only the lukewarm favor of President Madison, was not a man to let Perry sulk long. In fact, the very day the squadron arrived, he insisted that Perry accompany him to find proper anchorage.

Together they reconnoitered a bay landlocked on three sides by rocky shore line and protected to the north by a small, towering islet. Perry promptly christened it Put in Bay, and young Dulaney Forrest, acting lieutenant and Perry's chief signal officer on the *Lawrence*, said the isle reminded him of Gibraltar. Put in Bay and Gibraltar they were named.

As seamen from the *Lawrence* made soundings in the bay and across rocky openings into the lake, Perry agreed with Harrison that Gibraltar's impregnable seventy-foot cliff made Put in Bay easily defensible. Further, he said, the site was ideal for watching Barclay's movements out of Malden.

Since the suggestion had come from him in the first place, the general was delighted that the commodore approved his nautical recommendation.

Like Perry, Harrison was the kind of military man who wanted to fight, rather than feint in the manner of Chauncey and Sir James Yeo. The land and sea commanders found they hit it off splendidly, disagreeing on only one thing.

Barclay would just sit out the winter at Malden, Harrison said contemptuously. He knew that the fortress guns would protect his fleet and that the Americans couldn't move enough big guns across the ice to challenge him.

No, Perry argued, sooner or later Barclay would be forced out onto the lake to open a line of communication with the chief British supply base at Long Point. General Proctor would insist on it and when that happened, like it or not, Barclay would come out fighting for the showdown.

Harrison shrugged skeptically.

However, general and commodore were in complete agreement on their joint strategy for the invasion of Canada. When the time came, Perry would move Harrison's army to the Bass Islands, about eight miles from the mainland on a line with the water route to Malden.

Later, restudying the whole area, Perry changed his mind. He noticed that Middle Sister Island was located about halfway between Malden and Put in Bay. Surely this would be a more appropriate

PUT IN BAY

rendezvous for the army just before its attack, he told Harrison. Old Tippecanoe, who had developed complete faith in Perry, quickly agreed.

Two days later, accompanied by Colonels McArthur and Cass and Major Croghan, heroic defender of Fort Stephenson, General Harrison paid an official call aboard Perry's flagship.

But, like Perry, Harrison wasn't much of a man for wasting time on military formalities during war, and with him he brought 26 Indian chiefs. Actually, while the amenities were being observed, the general artfully impressed on the savages the awful power of Perry's "great canoes."

It came off nicely. Though they tried to remain stony-faced, the chiefs were awed by the great guns and billowing canvas. Chief Tarhe, of the Wyandots, even dispatched runners to Malden to tell his tribesmen to remain neutral.

Nor had Harrison neglected to note Perry's desperate need for marines and seamen. In a few days Perry was startled to see a strangely garbed contingent of 100 men arrive from McArthur's Brigade—a present from the general.

49

Kentucky sharpshooters all, the lanky frontiersmen wore blue linsey-woolsey hunting shirts, red belts, blue pantaloons fringed with red and fringed hunting jackets. Though they carried their long rifles with an air of lethal authority, they seemed like small children as they casually wandered through the *Lawrence*, ignoring Perry's officers, even invading his cabin, exclaiming in delight at the big guns.

For almost an hour, while the *Lawrence's* officers fumed at the outrage, Perry let them sight-see to their hearts' content. "These are independent backwoodsmen," he told the protesting young Forrest. "We must gentle them slowly." Then he mustered them on deck in a ragged line for a lecture on naval discipline and etiquette, and was somewhat taken aback to receive three rousing cheers instead of a respectful "Aye, aye, sir."

From Washington and Sackett's Harbor the news was good. Secretary Jones asked Perry to remain in command. So did the enigmatic Chauncey. He makes it sound for the record as though it were my fault in the first place that he had not—and still doesn't—give me the men, Perry thought.

None the less, he was relieved that he had been able to make Chauncey back down. Summoning Sam Hambleton, he told him the news and ordered, "Put the word out on the scuttle butts right away."

"Aye, gladly, sir. The men will cheer at hearing it straight that the commodore is staying. And I'll lead them!"

Late in August, Perry's squadron stood for Malden, but at the Detroit River, he prudently veered off. The wind changed unpredictably, and he didn't want to chance possible capture of his duller sailers.

"Thought we were going to beard them," young Lieutenant Stevens complained.

"We will, Mr. Stevens," Perry assured him. "It's our turn now."

A few days later, colors set and decks cleared for action, Perry returned. Now the wind was from the northeast, favorable for standing in and out of the river, and for a whole, delightful day the squadron mocked the British ships that were idle at their moorings.

It was sweet revenge, but, more important, Perry wanted a close look at the redoubtable *Detroit*. She was even more powerful than his spies had reported, with 19 guns of every calibre, 17 of them long ones, one mounted on a pivot.

"Quite a ship," Sailing Master William Taylor said with a forced casualness. "Full rigger with a lot of punch."

It was like a sailing master to be impressed with a full rigger, Perry thought. "Aye, mister," he said grudgingly, "a fine ship but roughly hewed. However, her bulwarks look heavy enough to withstand round shot fired at carronade range. And, notice you, she bristles with those long guns."

Taylor, leaning on the lee rail, studied the *Detroit* unhappily.

"She can—I have no doubt will—give us much trouble at long range," Perry said. "But we won't give her much chance for that. We'll take a close quarter raking position and, in spite of those bulwarks, give her hell with the big carronades."

Just then, young Lieutenant Forrest approached, saluting Perry with an easy grace. Perry returned it.

"I was just saying, Mr. Forrest, that short range is our only sound tactic here. What say you? You were with Bainbridge on *Old Ironsides* when she took the *Java* last year."

"Aye, sir. And I hope to be with the *Lawrence* when the *Detroit* strikes, too."

Eyes narrowed, the lieutenant appraised the big enemy warship now silently enduring the Yankee "bearding." For a full minute he was silent; then he turned, speaking almost apologetically to Perry. "Just one thing, sir. We must watch her extra-careful in a fight. With her punch and our thin sides and bulwarks, she could hull us through and through."

CHAPTER 6

Thursday, September 9, 1813

Commodore Perry slipped into his blue nankeen sailor's jacket, put his hat squarely on his head and stooped to study the open logbook on the desk in his little cabin.

He read the date aloud, shaking his head impatiently. Nearly a month now he had been on the lake, and still Barclay would not come out to meet him. Why it should be this day rather than any other he could not for the life of him explain. But the decision was suddenly clear in his mind.

He was going to give Barclay just twenty-four hours more to quit his cozy berth under Malden's guns—and then he would go after him.

He picked up his glass and walked on deck. The day had dawned warm and pleasant, and the sky was clear. Sea gulls wheeled in lazy circles over Put in Bay, uttering plaintive cries. Occasionally one plummeted toward the water, then rose with a fish in its beak.

Lifting his glass with restrained eagerness, Perry drew a line on Middle Sister Island, sighting toward the lane to Malden. Sky, water and nothing else. He let the glass drop to his side.

Perry heard footsteps, and then Dulaney Forrest greeted him. "Morning, sir." Anticipating the question, he added, "Sorry, sir."

"No sail?" Perry pressed.

"None, sir. We've kept a sharp lookout both here and on Gibraltar."

Perry slapped his glass against his thigh. "At least I managed to get some rest last night."

"I hope you're feeling better, sir. You looked pretty stove in last night."

"Aye. But I do feel better, and thank you, Mr. Forrest." He paused, then continued. "Soon now, Mr. Forrest—very much sooner than you realize—we will entice the reluctant Barclay from his snug moorings."

Taylor, the sailing master, reported to Perry. "Wind's shifting about, sir. Steadying from the southwest. We'd have to beat out of here against it if it freshens."

Perry nodded, almost absently.

"When was it we first stood for Malden, mister?"

To a young man, time flies fast. Forrest absently scratched his head. "More than two weeks ago, sir."

"And still the British hug Malden!" Perry exclaimed.

"I remember the date," Forrest said suddenly. "August twenty-fifth. It was the day that damned bilious fever decked you and half the men."

Perry nodded, tugging at a sideburn. "Decked Doc Parsons right along with the rest of us."

He winced.

"Did ye ever have one of Doc Parsons' plasters on your neck! Hot as hell itself and pulls like a whirlpool. Why it works, I'll never know. Fixed me up, though."

"Seems to me those attacks are getting worse," Forrest said, concern in his voice.

"Fresh water isn't meant for lads weaned on salt and sargasso

52

weed," Perry said lightly. "It's good salt air I need. But, meanwhile, the Doc is fixing me up."

He couldn't help grimacing at the thought of the devil's brew which the ship's surgeon called "tea," made from a foul root of some kind.

"The old faker says it's good for the belly," he explained.

Raising his voice, Perry roared, "Hannibal!" As the big Negro rushed up from below, Perry ordered, "Fetch me another pot of that bilge water Doc Parsons calls tea. My belly is kicking up again like a nor' easter."

"Yes, suh."

Brusquely Perry dismissed his men's concern. "Hannibal's just got to be kept doing something," he said.

Forrest wanted to know about Barclay's strength.

"Those refugees from Malden gave us accurate information at Sandusky Bar, I think. They have six vessels to our nine."

"Isn't it ten, sir?" Taylor interrupted.

"Nine. The *Ohio* will have to miss the fight. Mr. Dobbins has her over at Erie, loading stores."

"But the British ships are bigger?" Forrest asked.

"Generally, yes. Though our total tonnage is about seventeen hundred, Barclay's roughly fifteen hundred."

"And they outgun us?" Forrest persisted.

"I figure sixty-three guns and four howitzers," Perry said slowly.

"Against our fifty-four guns."

Perry smiled tightly. "Yes, we've fewer guns than Barclay, but we can fire more metal at close range. About three pounds to two, I'd say."

"Then it's about even," Taylor calculated, a note of relief in his voice.

"Save for cause, Mr. Taylor," Perry amended. "We have a cause. The British have only a grudge. That puts the advantage on our side."

A reeking smell interrupted them, and Hannibal approached, holding a small pot of tea almost at arm's length. "You black devil!" Perry said. "Suppose you had to drink it?"

He waited impatiently as the Negro filled a cup. He motioned for Hannibal to take the pitcher and tray to his cabin. Then, shuddering, he drained the cup and spat. "Filthy stuff!" he growled. "Why can't medicine ever taste like grog!"

Forrest was looking at him expectantly.

"Another question, Mr. Forrest? Out with it!"

"I was wondering, sir, whether and how you figure on striking Barclay if he stays under the guns at Malden?"

"I have made my decision, mister. If he doesn't show today, we will hit him at his anchorage tomorrow."

As to how, Perry explained, there would be a concerted attack with Harrison, a very risky one because the two forces would have to be separated. Slowly, testing the mettle of Forrest and Taylor with his words, he spelled out what a setback to either attacking force would mean.

If the fleet were defeated on the river, then the army hitting Malden from the land would find itself fighting not only the British army but also Barclay's guns. And if the army were repulsed, Perry's men would draw fire both from Barclay's guns and the big land batteries of the fort.

"Think it's worth the risk, misters?" he asked suddenly.

"Better than sitting on our sterns out here and just waiting," Forrest said.

"Aye," Taylor agreed. "But that full-rigged *Detroit* sure is some humdinger!"

Shortly before dark Perry ate alone in his cabin, patiently enduring Hannibal's coaxing that he should eat more. He didn't eat enough to keep a sea gull alive, the Negro fretted, and now his color was bad again. A big important man like the commodore should watch himself.

"Damn you! Fetch me some more of that bilge water, if you must, and then button those big elephant tusks! I've got to think."

"Yes, suh," Hannibal said in a relieved tone.

Perry sent his respects to Lieutenant John J. Yarnall, first officer of the *Lawrence*, asking him to report at once to his cabin. Yarnall, of course, already knew of the impending move, but Perry explained that he wanted a full-dress meeting with his commanders to give the final orders.

Yarnall left, promising to set the conference signal at once.

Soon, small boats converged on the *Lawrence* and Perry personally greeted each officer as he boarded. They clustered about on the deck, waiting for Elliott, last to arrive, though the *Niagara* was moored close by.

After the captain had finally exchanged cool greetings with Perry, they all adjourned down to the commodore's cabin. "Turn up the lamps, Hannibal," Perry ordered.

For a few moments there was silence as Perry studied them one by one, probing for some hidden flaw that might be pitilessly, disastrously exposed on the morrow. Elliott frowned faintly, and his eyes seemed almost sullen. I really don't quite know what to make of him, Perry thought, and yet by rank I *had* to give him the *Lawrence*.

The rest, though, satisfied him thoroughly. Turner, of the *Caledonia*, and Packett, of the *Ariel*, alertly watching his every move as they would do in battle. Solid, reliable Sailing Master Champlin, of the *Scorpion*, and Almey, of the *Somers*, soberly reading the final written instructions Perry had just handed out.

His eyes softened as he looked at young Stevens, of the *Trippe*, tense as a fighting cock in the ring, who was sitting alongside Marine Lieutenant John Brooks, posted to the *Lawrence*. And his other two lieutenants, Conklin, of the *Tigress*, and Senatt, of the *Porcupine*, already arguing whose long thirty-two would do the most damage.

Loudly, Perry cleared his throat. All conversation ceased and, except for the faint slapping of the waves against the hull and the eerie cry of some wild creature ashore on South Bass Island, there was complete silence. The officers turned expectantly toward him.

We who are about to die salute you, he thought with a swift ache as he looked at the young faces. Then quietly, almost prosaically, he read aloud the written instructions. Expanding on them, he detailed every contingency that he thought could conceivably arise and how he expected his forces to handle them.

Most of all, he emphasized, he planned to fight at close range, bringing the British alongside as soon as possible, so as not to lose the effectiveness of the big carronades. Slowly spacing out the words, he told them again:

"Engage your designated adversary in close action, gentlemen. Make it half a cable's length. Keep on the line, also at a half cable's length, from the vessel of our squadrons ahead of you. I cannot possibly advise you better than to repeat the words of a gentleman who would be our enemy, if he were alive and here tonight. '*If you lay your enemy alongside, you cannot be out of your place,*' Lord Nelson said."

Perry paused. He looked about expectantly, but there were no questions, and he beckoned the officers to follow him onto the deck.

Above, the full moon illuminated the splendid autumn night with a

55

pale light, and a soft southwestern breeze rocked the *Lawrence* almost imperceptibly. Even the younger officers were subdued, respectfully waiting for Perry to break the silence.

Deliberately, hoping that the night concealed the shaking of his hands, he removed the carefully folded battle flag from beneath his arm and unfurled it. As the officers gathered about the huge square of blue, a shaft of moonlight caught the foot-high muslin letters. In ghostly white, Jim Lawrence's legacy sprang alive before their eyes.

Don't give up the ship.

It was Perry's restrained voice that broke the spell. "Gentlemen, when this flag shall be hoisted to the *Lawrence's* main-royal masthead, it shall be the signal for you to go into action. Good night and good luck."

Perry remained at the ladder, personally shaking the hand of each departing officer. Then, as the last small boat pulled away, he returned to his cabin and tried to sleep.

But sleep did not come quickly. Memories crowded his mind, and something about the evening's conference nagged at him.

Though he tried to shut them out, there were disjointed recollections of his boyhood in Newport as he sailed toy boats in the shallow Pawcatuck River . . . Of the exciting but homesick days when he had first gone to Warren with his father to watch the *General Greene* being built . . . Of that sickening time his command had been wrecked and he had stood inquiry . . .

Then his mind raced forward to Presque Isle and all the frustrations he had endured the past six months—Chauncey's attitude . . . the grinding chore of building a squadron in a wilderness . . . the brief triumph when he had cameled the *Lawrence* and the *Niagara* over the bar, making nonsense of Elliott's defeatist predictions.

Elliott!

Now it came to him, and he sat up suddenly, banging his head against the *Lawrence's* curving side. That was what had been subconsciously nagging at him about tonight's battle conference. Though sullen, Elliott had not interposed one objection, had not once tried to belittle Perry in the others' eyes.

Perhaps, Perry thought comfortably, I squelched him once and for all the first time and he's come around. Then he felt a misgiving about Mr. Elliott. Perhaps he has some plan of his own, Perry speculated, and he is too crafty a man to commit himself aforehand. If that is so, we may have trouble tomorrow.

Finally he dropped off to sleep with an awkward prayer on his lips. "God give us the victory," he mumbled.

"Sail ho!"

The lookout's cry from the masthead brought Perry rolling from his bunk almost before he was awake. A moment later he heard Dulaney Forrest sing out, "Sail ho!" in jubilant echo, and then the lieutenant burst into Perry's cabin, forgetting the formality of knocking first.

"Sail ho!" he repeated. "Six of them off the northwestern board, sir. About Middle Sister, I'd say. They're standing for Put in Bay!"

"Good! At last!"

Perry had slept in his trousers. Now he needed to slip on only his boots and jacket to be fully dressed.

"What's the hour?"

"Just about five o'clock, sir. Barely sunrise."

"And the wind direction?"

"Still the southwest quarter, sir, but failing."

Perry made the calculations quickly in his mind. Off Middle Sister, and wind failing.

"Shall I make the signals, 'Enemy in Sight' and 'Under Way to Get,' sir?" Forrest asked excitedly.

Perry grinned as he straightened up and reached for his blue nankeen jacket. Somehow, now that the action was joining, he felt comfortable, almost relaxed. "Signal 'Enemy in Sight,' " he ordered. "But not yet 'Under Way to Get.' "

Surprise showed in Forrest's eyes.

"No hurry, mister. There's plenty of time ahead. At least two hours, I figure."

Perry slipped into the jacket, buttoned it deliberately as Forrest fidgeted, and reached for his hat and glass.

"I'm hungry, Mr. Forrest," he said. "But I'm still hungrier for the sight of those blasted British. Let us go out on deck and watch them coming to us at last. Then we will have a bit of breakfast. No telling when we will eat again today."

CHAPTER 7

As PERRY had predicted weeks earlier to General Harrison, Barclay's hand was being forced. American spies did not know that Amherstburg was so dangerously underprovisioned that there wasn't a day's flour in store, and the British tars were on half allowances. Barclay had to fight or starve.

Silently Perry's men watched the slow, tacking approach of the enemy fleet. With deliberation, Perry breakfasted and, from the calm expression on his face, none could have guessed the uneasy thoughts that now raced through his mind.

In lone-wolf seafights, American frigates had blasted to bits the legend of British invincibility on the water. But, under the more exacting demands of complicated mass maneuvers, could a Yankee fleet do likewise? Today would tell, and Perry's cherished naval career hung on the answer.

"All hands, up anchor!"

The command, echoing across the quiet reaches of Put in Bay, abruptly shattered the silence of the Yankee sailors.

Perry watched the signal flag, "Under Way to Get," sway up the halyard to the *Lawrence's* truck. "I've finished," he said, turning to Hannibal. "Take the rest of this chow back. You'd have me big as a full rigger."

The anchor thudded into position, and the *Lawrence* suddenly came to life with the free-feeling motion of a ship no longer under restraint. Sweating men scrambled aloft to begin unfurling the big brig's white towers of canvas.

"It will be a fight, beating our way out of here against this wind," Perry said to Dulaney Forrest. "The schooners and gunboats will have to use sweeps and oars. I hope we can pass to windward of Green and Rattlesnake islands."

As he watched his men clearing the *Lawrence's* decks for action, six bells sounded. "Seven o'clock already, mister?"

Forrest nodded.

Now the British vessels were plainly visible and, with his glass, Perry could even see the topmen scrambling about in the *Detroit's* rigging. None the less, the two fleets were barely crawling toward each other. It had been a full two hours since they first had sighted the enemy sail, and the breeze from the southwest quarter was light, unsteady and failing.

Impatiently Perry passed an order to Forrest, and the young signal officer bent on additional flags. Shortly the *Niagara* and *Lawrence* were being aided by oarsmen in small boats out ahead, while the smaller vessels were using sweeps and oars.

They made the lee of Gibraltar after slow, inching progress, but beating to the windward of Green and Rattlesnake islands was proving impossible. Perry cursed under his breath.

The maneuver was critically important to him. It would give him a leading breeze to run down on the enemy and the precious weather gauge in the battle. Three times his vessels strained to cross the channel, and three times they were headed off and forced to tack.

"How much more time will it take to weather the islands, mister?" Perry asked Sailing Master Taylor.

"Difficult to say, sir, what with the breeze unsteady like this."

Again they tried. Apprehensively Perry watched a rain squall moving rapidly toward them from the southwest. Soon the big drops were drumming through the *Lawrence's* stiff new canvas, and the men aloft cursed as the lines became treacherously slippery.

Then, as four bells sounded, the storm blew over, the sky quickly cleared and blazing sunlight bathed the *Lawrence's* deck again.

"Wear ship," Perry said in exasperation. "We'll run to the leeward of the islands."

"But that means we will have to engage the enemy to the leeward, sir," Taylor objected.

"Aye, Mr. Taylor. That we will. To windward, leeward or damnward, they'll fight today!"

Taylor bawled the orders, and new flags swayed up the signal halyard.

The *Lawrence*, sailing close-hauled, was brought to the new tack by putting her helm up and turning her head away from the wind.

A few minutes later Perry lifted his head sharply. "The wind shifts."

Young Forrest studied the broad commander's pennant at the *Lawrence's* truck. "Southeast," he called out exuberantly. "And freshening!"

Taylor yelled new orders which, punctuated by the shrill, urgent shriekings of boatswains' whistles, were repeated on all ships. All sails set, the fleet bore away to the windward of the islands and stood off briskly in the direction of the enemy.

The crews fell to vigorously, casting guns loose, drawing supplies, balls, grape and canister, arranging pikes and cutlasses, hammering flints and lighting matches. Petty officers and officers armed themselves with pistols and cutlasses.

Perry smiled briefly as he watched Lieutenant John Brooks line up his makeshift marines from Kentucky who were fondling their long rifles and not paying overly respectful attention to their officer's words. Then he sent for his sword.

With the battle preparations swirling about him, Perry strolled to the starboard bulwark and studied the disposition of his squadron. Believing that the *Queen Charlotte* would lead the British line, he had placed the *Niagara*, her designated adversary, at the head of his own forces.

The *Ariel* and *Scorpion* followed, and then the *Lawrence*. Astern the flagship were the *Caledonia*, *Somers*, *Porcupine* and finally the slow-moving *Trippe*. Young Stevens, he guessed, was already burning with anxiety that he might be left behind.

The breeze died to fitful puffs, and though all sails were sheeted home, the *Lawrence* barely moved. Here and there, tars were gathered in little knots on the deck, asking each other to notify their families and to take care of their effects "just in case." Brother Jimmy returned with Perry's sword and, after girding it on, the commodore sent the boy back again to fetch the battle flag from the sea chest in his cabin.

He passed an order to Taylor, and the sailing master bellowed, "All hands assemble aft."

Respectful, yet eager, the men crowded about to listen to their commander. When Jimmy had brought him the flag, Perry unfurled it carefully, holding it high so that all the men could see it.

"My lads, this flag contains the last words of Captain Lawrence! Shall I hoist it?"

There was an enthusiastic chorus. "Aye, aye, sir!"

Perry himself bent it on the halyard rove to the top of the foreroyal and swayed it aloft. Cheers rose now from the other vessels, too, as the light breeze gently ruffled the blue field.

Next, Perry sent Jimmy to find Usher Parsons, the surgeon, and Sam Hambleton and bring them to the captain's cabin. He was studying the last three letters from his wife Elna when the two friends entered.

Perry stuffed the letters, along with a number of official papers, into a lead box and handed it to Parsons.

"You will throw this overboard, sir, in the event anything happens. That is, in the event we fail. . . ."

Parsons nodded soberly.

To Hambleton he gave a sealed, wax-encrusted packet. "My old friend, here are instructions for arranging my personal affairs in the event of my death. Will you see to it, please?"

Matter-of-factly Hambleton stuffed the packet inside his jacket. "Glad to oblige, Oliver," he said. "And I'll be sure to return it when the battle's over."

The three men laughed to bridge the awkward moment, and then went out into the bright September sunlight to watch final preparations.

With his glass, Perry studied the British vessels, newly caulked and painted, their hulls gleaming black with yellow and white port bands. However, the inner bulwarks and fighting stations were a deep crimson: Nelson's old trick, Perry remembered, for hiding the blood.

He looked thoughtfully at his own deck. Sailors had already wet it down with water and now were strewing sand so the men wouldn't slip on the blood during battle. A grisly but necessary preparation.

By now, Barclay had given up all hope of obtaining the weather gauge, and his ships were hove to in close order on a battle line on a port tack. Heading south and west, they were about nine miles west of Put in Bay, Perry calculated. That would put them about the same distance from the mainland and maybe six miles distant from his approaching squadron.

With professional admiration he watched Barclay's skillful maneuvering to take every advantage offered by the lee gauge. A good seaman and a tough opponent. He had positioned his ships so they would rake the Americans as they bore down while the Yankees would be able to retaliate only with their bow chasers.

Through the mass of flying pennants and multicolored flags, Perry saw that the *Chippewa* was leading the British line. In order, the *Detroit, Hunter, Queen Charlotte, Lady Prevost* and *Little Belt* followed.

That meant an immediate readjustment of his own formation. He told Forrest to signal the *Niagara* to drop back, taking a position between the *Caledonia*, just astern of the *Lawrence*, and the schooners.

That would properly position her to attack the *Queen Charlotte*, and then, since the *Ariel* was without bulwarks, he signaled her to move on his weather bow for partial cover. Perry watched the *Niagara* closely, but Elliott executed the maneuver smartly and quickly, and Perry relaxed. The *Ariel* followed into her new position without incident.

Now he was satisfied. The *Ariel's* long guns, together with those of the *Scorpion* and *Caledonia*, would help supply the power he needed against the massive *Detroit*—at least until he could get within carronade range.

From below decks some of the men in the sick bay came up to offer him their services. Perry was touched. He realized that the scuttlebutt had gone around that he was ailing from the fever again. He thanked each man individually, but recommended that their best course was to rest until he summoned them.

As grog and bread bags were broken out for lunch, Perry ordered Hannibal to fetch him another pot of Doc Parsons' tea. He drank a cup, grimacing in spite of himself. "I trust the day will be sweeter," he growled to young Forrest.

By the time he had managed to down a second cup, fife and drum were sounding to quarters. Whether it was Parsons' magic or his own imagination, he didn't know, but some of the fever weakness seemed to diminish.

Gun by gun, he inspected the batteries, starting with the *Constitution* gunners. They stood arrayed beside the bulbous, thirty-two-pound larboard carronades, as big as *Old Ironsides* herself carried, and Perry felt comforted at the sight of them.

"Well, lads, are you ready?" he asked, knowing that the question was rhetorical.

"All ready, your honor." As each repeated the phrase, he respectfully touched the bandanna girding his forehead.

"I needn't say more. You best know how to beat those fellows. I have it on good authority direct from the *Guerrière!*"

"Aye, aye, sir!"

For the men whom he himself had trained back at the Newport Station there was a special warmth in his voice. "My own Newport lads! You'll do your duty today, I warrant."

"Aye, aye, your honor."

"The Union Jack's in trouble this day," a young Negro piped up.

As his companions roared at his audacity, Perry moved closer, whacking the lad on his shining, dusky back. "Well spoken!"

During the last half-hour, an expectant hush had settled over the

Lawrence, and Perry could hear the creak of green timbers, the faint shrieking of the wind in the riggings aloft. Loudly, seven bells sounded. Eleven-thirty already! Where had the time gone?

Reviewing his squadron through his glass, he found the vessels were at least up on station, though the schooners were vigorously using sweeps and oars to maintain their positions. All, that is, except the poor-sailing *Trippe*, which now trailed a good two miles astern.

Poor Stevens, Perry thought. The boy must be beside himself now.

Ahead, the six enemy vessels were lying stationary, dipping and rising gently on the smooth swell, as though moored for peacetime inspection.

Suddenly dispelling the illusion, band music broke out on all six British ships, and then a bugle from the *Detroit* abruptly commanded silence.

A puff of smoke erupted from the great vessel, to the accompaniment of cheers, and a blast crackled across the water toward the *Lawrence*. Thirty feet away a waterspout signaled the long gun's near miss.

Eleven-forty-five. The action was joined.

"Steady as she goes, lads," Perry bellowed through the speaking trumpet. "Steady now. Bear up."

A second gun on the *Detroit* puffed blue smoke. Splinters hissed through the air as the round shot crashed through both bulwarks of the *Lawrence*, and a seaman screamed. Perry saw tars gently carrying the casualty below to Doc Parsons.

"Barclay wants this fight at a distance," he said. "He has long-gun superiority. I have a surprise for him. We're going right through to close carronade range.

The *Lawrence* moved ahead gently at about three knots, but the gunboats, unable to keep their places in line in the fitful breeze, were beginning to fall back beyond effective range.

Then the *Scorpion's* long gun hurled a despairing salvo that whistled through the *Detroit's* riggings.

"Hard-a-lee," Perry said. "Canister will be screaming by our stern sheets soon enough now."

Again, round shot from the *Detroit* long guns plunged through the *Lawrence*, and the brig shuddered. Perry counted ten hits. Still he waited.

Enveloped in her own gunsmoke, the *Detroit* loomed steadily closer, her long guns stepping up the fierce punishment. Canister and chain shot furrowed the *Lawrence's* pine deck and ripped her sails. Men screamed and fell, clutching themselves in the bloody sand. Others, shot in two, dropped lifelessly without a moan.

Finally Perry decided they were within musket range.

"Fire!"

The big thirty-two-pound carronades roared, and from the *Ariel*, *Caledonia* and *Niagara*, long twelves opened fire. But the *Niagara*, Perry saw with dismay, was keeping at a respectful distance from the enemy.

"Barclay plans to knock us out of action first," he bellowed to Forrest and Hambleton. "Then he would take the others, one by one."

He called to the sailing master. "Lay the *Detroit* close alongside, Mr. Taylor!"

Taylor touched his cap with his hand.

"Fire when ready on the guns."

Double-shotted, the *Lawrence's* heavy carronades thundered their metal into the *Detroit's* heavy bulwarks. Aloft, there was the lighter rattle of musketry as the Kentucky sharpshooters, perched in the riggings, calmly picked off British tars as though they were squirrels.

Now lead and iron raked the *Detroit* fore and aft, splintering spars and masts, shredding sail and rigging. Perry wasted no time in gloating. His own bulwarks were giving way before the *Detroit's* pounding, and much of the *Lawrence's* rigging was hanging limp and useless.

CHAPTER 8

IN THE flagging wind the *Lawrence* moved slowly, even under full sail. As she sluggishly closed with the *Detroit*, round shot hulled her through and through, punishing mast, frame and sails, raising waterspouts that gushed aboard to mingle with the blood.

Barclay was so determined to blow her sky-high that he ignored the little *Ariel* and *Scorpion*. A blessing, Perry thought, for the two smaller vessels were maintaining a steady and damaging fire. Now, if only the *Niagara* would join the battle which was becoming general along the line!

64

Perry studied his squadron's disposition through the bluish-gray haze that all but obscured the ships. The *Trippe* still was not up, no fault of Stevens. But the *Niagara*, strangely, was using only one long gun. He couldn't understand it.

With an oath the Commodore directed the bugler to sound the order for all ships to put on sail and come alongside their designated adversaries.

"Starboard batteries doing well, sir," Lieutenant Yarnall reported, briefly touching his cap.

Though the lieutenant's features were smoke-blackened, Perry could see dismay, curiosity, anger on his face.

"Beg pardon, sir, but what the hell's keeping the *Niagara*? If she doesn't bear a hand soon, the *Queen Charlotte* will be hammering at us, too. And we've already got our hands full."

Perry shook his head noncommittally. He had his private opinion of Captain Elliott, but he hesitated to voice it.

He beckoned to his sailing master and shouted a new order above the thunder.

"Crowd on all sail, Mr. Taylor. We'll run down and close with them. Can't wait any longer on the *Niagara*." Impulsively he blurted, "She ignores my orders!"

Through his speaking trumpet Taylor relayed the command and, agitated as he was, Perry could not help but admire the expert execution by his topmen. Only weeks ago, some of these agile monkeys aloft had been completely strange to all shipboard procedure. Now they seemed as sure of themselves as old Newport tars.

Perry directed the bugler to sound "Close." He watched, but the *Niagara* still kept her careful distance. Damn him, Perry thought, nervously running his hand through his dark hair. This is Elliott's revenge. Now I understand why he was silent at last night's battle conference.

Unmolested, the *Queen Charlotte* sheeted home additional sail, and began moving smoothly to the *Detroit's* assistance. Desperately the *Lawrence* luffed up, trying to get parallel to the big ship before the *Charlotte* could intervene.

At least, Perry noted grimly, his thirty-two's were pounding the life out of their target, and the Kentuckians' precise musket fire was devastating. As the two hulks drifted closer together, musket balls thudded close to him, but he was lost in the mathematics of the moment.

He counted off the guns that were trained on his flagship: 19 from the *Detroit*, 10 from the *Hunter*, 17 from the approaching *Charlotte*. Forty-six in all—and 24 of them working on him in a broadside! In return, he was firing ten-gun broadsides.

Sick with the answer that he reached, he momentarily closed his eyes. Forty-six to ten. He couldn't hold out! But he must delay—delay if it cost every life abroad the *Lawrence*.

Three times Yarnall, his face now gory from a raking scalp wound, his nose splinter-pierced and swollen, came to him for more men and got them. Perry kept constantly in motion, sloshing back and forth through bloody sand, encouraging the men, trying to set them a steadying example.

His white breeches were black with powder, his hat was lost, and his clothing sweat-soaked and blood-spattered. But his bearing was cool, and occasionally he managed a tight smile.

"It's Lieutenant Brooks, sir." Forrest's young face was white and anguished. "He's . . . he's calling for you."

Near the after larboard bulwarks where the Marine officer had dropped, Perry found him, smashed and broken. His handsome face was gray; his lips were bleeding where he had bitten them to stifle his screams of pain. Directing his marines' musket fire, he had caught a round shot square in the hip, and all his lower body was a mass of bloody flesh and splintered bone.

"Shoot me, sir! I beg it of you. Forrest won't. Please, sir, end this pain."

Perry spoke almost gruffly, trying to keep the pity out of his voice. "Brace up, mister." He turned to two seamen nearby. "Take Mr. Brooks below to the wardroom, lads. And . . . and find the chaplain for him, will you?"

Trying to clear the lump from his throat, he went back to the starboard batteries. Behind, he heard a single scream as the seamen lifted Brooks's broken body, and he winced. Last night the young officer had sat across from him, behind the little table in his cabin.

Perry patted Dulaney Forrest consolingly and, as he did so, the lieutenant grunted, his eyes widening in surprise, and he fell heavily into the dirty red sand. Not Forrest, too!

"Are you hit, Mr. Forrest?"

Forrest moved his head, then his dazed eyes cleared, and he got up uncertainly with Perry's help.

"I . . . I don't think so, sir."

He put his hand inside his coat, fishing out a grapeshot. He stared blankly at the spent missile, then dropped it into his pocket. "No, God be thanked, not hurt, sir. But this is my shot."

Perry heard the loud sucking noise of boots in the sticky mess underfoot, and Yarnall was alongside him again. All the men and officers of his division were done in. As he spoke, a round shot smashed through a *Constitution* gunner, and the man fell silently at Perry's feet.

Might he have more men? Yarnall asked, ignoring the casualty.

"I have no more," Perry said dully. "I have used every man, sick and well, even those assigned to aid Doc Parsons. I have no more."

"Aye, aye, sir." Alone, Yarnall plodded doggedly back toward his division. Three times wounded, Perry thought wonderingly, and still he fights like a hellcat.

Then he remembered Brooks, and descended the ladder to the wardroom. The dying lieutenant's eyes fluttered open and tried to focus as Perry gently called his name.

"Pain gone?"

"Aye, sir."

Perry forced himself to smile.

"Your Kentucky marines are doing excellently, sir. A credit to your training and the Marines."

Doc Parsons approached. Brooks made a feeble gesture of dismissal. "Look to the fit, Doctor. I am a dead man."

Slowly his eyes turned back toward Perry. "Thank you, sir. But how goes the day?"

"We are winning," Perry lied.

"Where is the *Niagara*?" Brooks demanded, fighting the dimness in his eyes. "Why doesn't she come down and help us?"

He knows, Perry thought. This good, brave officer knows that we are losing and must die knowing that, die with the ashy taste of defeat in his mouth. It isn't right!

Perry knelt alongside Brooks, gripping his arm tightly. "I intend to have this day, Mr. Brooks," he said fiercely. "You will not have suffered for naught. Do you hear me, mister? We will win! This I promise you."

For a moment a flash of spirit lighted the glazed eyes, and then Brooks's head fell back heavily.

Perry rose, bracing himself a moment against Forrest and then quickly climbed the ladder to the splintered deck.

Forrest followed. "He's right, sir! Where is Elliott? He's violating every rule of naval warfare by leaving his flagship unprotected!"

67

Perry turned with his glass to keep from answering. Through the layers of bluish smoke, he finally found the *Niagara*. Now her main yard was braced sharp back! Elliott was refusing to range past the *Caledonia*.

"What in the name of God is he doing, sir?" Now it was Yarnall complaining about Elliott. "Why doesn't he come to range and relieve us?"

Somehow, Perry felt, he must restrain himself till he could call Elliott to an accounting. "Some curious error, Mr. Yarnall."

"Error my toplight!" Yarnall, mopping his slashed scalp with a bloody kerchief, roared out the forthright contempt of a real fighting man. "Never saw more deliberate sailing."

"Let's bear a hand now," Perry said evasively, "and see what can be done at the moment."

Yarnall laughed bitterly. "The Commodore is too much of a gentleman, sir," he boomed. "The dog ought to be hung from a yardarm!"

"Easy as she goes, Mr. Yarnall." Perry spoke sharply. "The day isn't finished yet."

But, as the blasting, splintering, blood-bathed nightmare only worsened, he realized that the *Lawrence* certainly was finished.

Try as he might, he could not keep the big carronades going. He found men, wounded but still partly able, to drag the heavy guns back to their mounts, and then the recoil dismounted them again. One by one, they fell silent, and suddenly none were firing. British metal was screaming into a ghost ship.

Then one of Yarnall's carronades roared unexpected defiance, and Perry turned in surprise. The blodied first officer now was straining, almost alone, to get back into position. Perry looked about despairingly. "Are there any that can yet pull a rope?"

Several wounded seamen tried to crawl along the slippery deck toward him. He waved them back and himself moved toward the gun. Hambleton appeared suddenly out of the smoke and put his shoulder against the carronade as Perry, Yarnall and the chaplain tugged it back into mount position.

Yarnall rammed home the powder wad, and Perry choked the weapon with a double-shotted load. He touched the match to her, the big gun thundered, then recoiled off the mount. Commodore and first officer looked blankly at each other. Neither said anything.

Only two and a half hours, Perry thought miserably, and my new flagship lies dead in the water in her first engagement. Slowly, item by item, he inventoried the destruction.

Scuppers choked with human hair and brains and deck swimming in blood . . . bits of cloth, flesh and bone strewn everywhere. Rigging shot clean away, hanging or dragging astern. Spars splintered, all braces and bowlines out, bulwarks broken . . .

Worst, he heard, from the wardroom below, the cries of the wounded and dying, and counted the human toll. Twenty-two dead men on deck and 61 wounded below, according to Doc Parsons. That made 83 casualties. Only 16 men, young Jimmy and himself left then! Dear God, he asked, was I justified?

Somehow, Yarnall had again mounted one of the ponderous carronades, and found a gunner to ram home the powder. She was aimed dead at the *Detroit*, only half a pistol shot away. Handing the smouldering match to Perry, the first officer asked, "Care to do the honors, sir?"

Yarnall knew. Perry knew. This would be the *Lawrence's* last shot, and overdue by an hour. That long, she had been a beaten ship.

Perry touched the match to fuse and braced himself. The roar and simultaneous recoil were the *Lawrence's* requiem.

Despair and shame on his face, Yarnall came close to Perry, almost as though he wanted no one else to hear his question. "Shall we strike, sir?"

"No." God, how the big first officer hated to ask it, Perry thought with a twinge of pity. He pointed to the blue battle flag fluttering at the *Lawrence's* truck. "Bring it down," he said slowly. He wheeled sharply on Forrest. "Bring it down, Mr. Forrest! Roll it carefully and give it to me."

Forrest looked stunned, and Yarnall's face fell. Perry saw the pain in Sam Hambleton's eyes.

"You're quitting, sir?" Yarnall asked.

Ignoring the question, Perry turned to little Jimmy. "Check the small boat at our stern, mister, and see if it is still seaworthy. If so, have Hannibal and two other men lower it away. Then bring it to the port gangway."

"Aye, aye, sir." Jimmy sped aft, Hannibal lumbering along behind him.

"You're leaving us, sir?" Yarnall persisted. "Leaving the *Lawrence?*"

"Aye, Mr. Yarnall, leaving the *Lawrence*, but not quitting the fight!"

69

"I don't understand, sir. I'm afraid . . . my head . . . I'm not thinking very clearly."

"We can still turn the day, Mr. Yarnall, with the *Niagara*—if I can reach her in the small boat."

CHAPTER 9

Even in desperate moments, Oliver Hazard Perry did not like to be hurried. While the small boat was being readied, he went to his cabin, stripped off his battle-grimed clothing and changed into new pants and his epauletted uniform jacket. He came back on deck to find Yarnall, his head wounds now crudely bandaged, staring angrily toward the *Niagara*, a full half mile to windward.

"She's still not damaged at all that I can see," Perry admitted after studying her with his glass. "Not even a shot through her sails, and I don't believe she's fired anything but her long gun, either. I must confess I can't explain it. I thought at first she might have suffered rudder damage. I shall certainly have a talk with Mr. Elliott."

Now the *Niagara* was passing windward of the *Caledonia* in a line which was carrying her still further from the action.

Perry swore. "He's keeping to windward with her so as to use the *Lawrence* as shelter!" He turned to Yarnall. "Damned but you seem right, sir! He's firing regularly at the *Queen Charlotte* with his long twelve and steering for the head of the British line."

"He might as well be out of it altogether," Yarnall said disgustedly. "I don't even know if you can catch her, sir. It will take good oarsmen."

"I must! She's fresh and her magazines are filled with shot and powder. We still can turn the day with her."

"We're done, sir," Yarnall said tonelessly. "Guns dismounted, the breechings gone and the carriages hammered to bits."

"You have performed nobly, Mr. Yarnall, and yet I must ask one thing more. Keep the colors flying as long as humanly possible! It buoys up the lads on the other vessels. Try at least to keep them aloft until I raise my battle flag on the *Niagara*."

Yarnall's tired eyes lighted up. If only he could do that, only hold out until the commander were ready to fight again, there would be less shame in striking.

Forrest touched Perry's shoulder and sighted with his forefinger. "It's the *Lady Prevost*, sir. She's helpless. She's lost her rudder."

"So she has!" Perry said, feeling a lift of confidence.

Even the *Detroit*, though she still poured cruel metal into the helpless *Lawrence*, was firing almost in desperation now. Many of her braces had been cut away, and her mizzen topmast and gaff were badly damaged. Almost disabled, Perry judged.

Aye, and the *Queen Charlotte* seemed in even worse shape to Perry as he studied her through his glass. Barely manageable, it seemed, and the *Scorpion*, *Ariel* and *Caledonia* still hammering away at her. Good!

"I believe the wind is freshening, Mr. Forrest. If I can make the *Niagara*, I can clap on a full press of canvas and bear down to cut the British line."

"Aye, sir. The small boat is alongside. Good luck, sir, and God be with you."

Perry shook hands with him, then with Yarnall and, as he moved to port gangway, with Sam Hambleton. "You take good care, sir," said Sam. "This is a risky business. They'll be shooting at you proper."

"Remember my instructions, Sam, if anything should happen."

Impulsively Sam clasped Perry's hand with both of his big, rough hands. "I tell you again, sir. I'll be returning them this night after the British strike."

Dulaney Forrest looked hopefully at his commander. "Could I go with you, sir?"

"Best stay with Mr. Yarnall," Perry said regretfully. "He's lost some blood, and soon may need a strong hand at the helm."

Leaning over the bulwark, Perry saw Hannibal Collins holding the small boat away from the *Lawrence's* blood-slippery sides. Two seamen were manning the oars.

"Where's young Mr. Perry?" the Commodore asked sharply. "I left him with you."

"Excuse me, sir, but Mr. Perry's been hit."

Oh God, Perry thought, how will I write this to Mother?

"Not bad, sir," Hannibal continued hastily. "Jus' hit by a flyin' hammock torn loose from its netting by a round shot, sir."

"Here he is, sir!" a cheerful voice sang out from behind.

Young Seaman Thomas Penny was helping Jimmy toward the port

71

gangway. The boy's neck and left arm were bandaged, and he looked dazed.

"Caught a coupla splinters and a few small flyin' pieces, sir." Jimmy's voice was proud. Aged twelve, he had been blooded. "Just stunned a bit, sir. Doc Parsons fixed me up."

Perry felt a moment of profound gratefulness to God. That his brother, his good friend Sam, Doc Parsons, Yarnall, Forrest, himself had come through the holocaust almost unscathed was a miracle, and miracle was a word that Perry never used loosely.

Like Forrest, young Penny was looking hopefully at Perry. "I'll help him in the boat, sir," he volunteered. "And then go along, if it's all right with the Commodore, sir."

"Aye, lad. Get about it then."

Perry quickly turned to face the small knot of unwounded seamen gathered to watch the departure. "Let's have three more strong backs, lads. We'll need them for the oars to catch Captain Elliott now."

Half a dozen surged toward the port gangway. Perry, selecting the first three, raised his hand. "Enough."

Seaman Hosca Sargent came up with the battle flag which he had removed from the halyard and handed it to Perry. Just before descending to the small boat, Perry turned to Yarnall. "I leave it to your discretion to strike or not, as seems best," he said simply.

As he started down, Yarnell, Forrest and the grimy, surviving seamen came smartly to attention and saluted. There was a lump in Perry's throat, and he moved quickly to the small boat's stern sheets.

For a moment, he defiantly held up the blue silk flag as the *Lawrence's* men cheered. Then, throwing it over his left shoulder, he pointed to the distant *Niagara*. "Pull away, lads. Lively, now! Penny, fend off that wreckage. Jimmy, you sit down. You've been a hero once today. Pull, men!"

Soon as they cleared the lee of the *Lawrence*, Perry knew, they would be under direct fire. Uneasily, he felt a freshening breeze that was beginning to sweep away the fragile concealment of battle smoke.

"Please sit down, suh," Hannibal pleaded. "Ole Barclay's gonna throw everything but his binnacle at us, suh. Ain't no use you standin' up."

Perry, lost in calculations, ignored him.

Though the Americans did not know it, the British top command was suffering heavily. Almost at the outset of the fight, Captain Finnis, of the *Charlotte*, Barclay's good right hand, had fallen. Soon after, Lieutenant Stokes was knocked out by a splinter, and the big ship was now in the command of Provincial-Lieutenant Irvine, courageous, enthusiastic, but inexperienced.

Aboard the *Lady Prevost*, Lieutenant Buchan was gravely wounded and, as the day wore on, every commander, every second in command on all six British ships, was either killed or too badly hurt to keep the deck.

"Please, sir," young Jimmy said anxiously. "No use exposing yourself that way."

Vaguely Perry realized that now the British were beginning to train their fire on the small boat. From both sides waterspouts showered the passengers, and he wiped his eyes.

Then musket balls thudded into the craft's side, making the oarsmen feather. From the *Detroit* a full broadside of grape and canister whistled close overhead, boiling the water just beyond them.

Jimmy rose, vainly clutching at his brother with both hands. Then the oarsmen suddenly stopped rowing, and Perry realized what they meant. He sat down. The small boat spurted briskly forward.

Astern, the *Lawrence*, completely unmanageable, was falling behind, but the *Scorpion* still was firing both guns, and the three long twelves of the *Caledonia* were roaring steadily. The *Ariel* had three of her four in action.

As they passed the three vessels, seamen turned anxious faces toward the small boat, and Perry, waving the battle flag, gestured toward the *Niagara*. Cheers broke out and, it seemed to him, the pace of the firing was stepped up. The men had understood.

Jimmy touched his arm. "New signal flags on the *Niagara*," he said. Perry trained his glass on her rakish, intact mast.

"He's signaling someone to bear up and make away," he said bitterly. "The *Caledonia*, I figure. He'll have a time getting Turner to quit the fight."

Quickly the *Caledonia* responded to the signal—by making all sail for the enemy's line. "Good man, Turner! He's going to defend the *Lawrence*. By God, he'll board the *Detroit* before he'll run away!"

By now they had covered more than half the distance to the *Niagara*, and the hot musket fire directed at them had ceased. The *Detroit's* longs still lobbed canister after them, but the fire was falling short. Perry allowed himself to relax.

As they moved under the *Niagara's* port quarter, he looked at his watch. Two forty-six.

With a helpful boost from Hannibal, he clambered aboard, and Elliott, immaculate in epauletted uniform, hurried forward nervously to greet him.

Perry felt such a fury throbbing in his head that he had to clench his hands behind his back. He was afraid he would hit the man.

"What is the result on your brig?" Elliott asked placatingly.

"Shot to pieces, Mr. Elliott! Shot to smithereens! By God, sir, today I have been sacrificed most shamefully!"

With superhuman effort, he restrained himself. The *Niagara's* tars were looking curiously at the two commanders. A row on deck in front of them would be unforgivable and, anyhow, Perry mistrusted that he could withhold his fists if an argument developed.

Coldly he craned his neck to stare up through the *Niagara's* five successive tiers of canvas. Sails and rigging perfectly secure! His eyes raked the deck, unsplintered, unbloodied, and the seamen behind the big carronades, clean-faced and fresh. They had not fired a shot! Only the tars on the long twelve had powder-blackened faces.

Again, the fury made his head throb worse than the fever had, and he thought, I must control myself, I must, I must!

Turning to Elliott, he said shortly, "The breeze has been poor, and the gunboats could not get into the early action."

"Shall I go and bring them up?" Elliott asked nervously.

"You may do so, " Perry said curtly. "By all means, do so!" He wanted the man out of his sight.

Elliott scuttled off, and Perry thought disdainfully, my second in command, second officer of the fleet, off on a needless errand with a superfluous message. The order could as easily have been signaled, but now the gunboats were advancing as quickly as possible with sweeps and oars. Good riddance, though, to Mr. Elliott!

He shook his head vigorously, as though to shake the man out of his mind, and handed his battle flag to the *Niagara's* signal officer. Run it to the masthead, sir, and hoist the signal for close action."

Something almost as hot and real as a charge of electricity flamed through the idle brig, and from the other American vessels cheers rose as the shot-pierced blue battle flag swayed aloft again.

Listening intently, Perry imagined that he could hear faint cheers even from the drifting *Lawrence*. His glass picked out her truck, and his face saddened. The colors were gone. She had struck.

Roughly he grasped a speaking trumpet from a seaman and as the small boat carrying Elliott drew away, bellowed the orders so very long overdue. "Back up the main topsail and brail up the main trysail! Put the helm up to run down before the wind! Alter your course eight points. Square the yards there! Set the foresail, topsail and topgallants."

On deck and aloft, in a happy, scrambling, yet efficient mass motion, the men obeyed. And then Perry shouted the order that sent cheers racing down the line of gunners and echoing from the masts above. "Bear down sharply now to cut the British line!"

Leaving the quarter-deck, Perry began checking the guns. The *Niagara* almost leaped as her canvas caught the breeze, her lee rail dropping lower, her stern churning up bubbly white wake behind.

"Check your flints and matches, lads. Ready powder wads and shot. We're going to hold fire until we can rake them as we cut their line."

Six bells sounded as he returned to the quarter-deck. He studied the sun. Only three o'clock? Only fourteen minutes? In that time the *Niagara* had been transformed from a pretty brig into a Yankee fighting ship.

The *Detroit* had ceased firing and was trying to wear ship. Sluggishly the *Queen Charlotte* ranged up on her.

"They're going to foul!" Perry said aloud. "Sure as hell they're going to, Mr. Forrest!"

Then he remembered. Poor Forrest, if still alive, was back on the *Lawrence*, a British prisoner.

For a moment Perry felt very lonely, but the mood passed as he watched the *Charlotte* run her head booms and bowsprit hard into the *Detroit's* mizzen rigging. Exultantly he saw gunners scurrying from their stations to fend off and disentangle after the collision. Good! Good!

And on the *Detroit's* weather quarter, more trouble was piling up for her. In the action at last, young Stevens was moving the *Trippe* into position. Knowing the young cock, Perry calculated he would board the full-rigger with the impetuosity he had shown on the Niagara frontier. Perry frowned. Hoped the young hothead wouldn't be too reckless.

Now, after long hours, all of Perry's fleet was in the fight, except for the lost *Lawrence*. The three British capital ships could not sail; the *Queen Charlotte* and the *Detroit* were lashed together. The *Lady Prevost* was unmanageable without her rudder.

Perry put down his elation. Now, more than ever, he must be cool, plan the right course and wring the ultimate from the enemy's distress.

Let's see how we will do it, he said to himself. The *Detroit* and the *Queen Charlotte* on our starboard, the *Chippewa* and *Lady Prevost* on larboard. As the boatswain's mates strained to catch and relay the command, he picked up the speaking trumpet. "Ready on the guns! Stand by!"

"Aye, aye, sir."

"Shorten sail!"

Her wake flattening suddenly, the *Niagara* slowed her headlong plunge as the topmen furled sail briskly. She edged easily through the British line under the bows of the *Detroit* and across the *Lady Prevost's* stern.

Just as Perry gave the order to fire, the *Detroit* and the *Queen Charlotte* were working free of each other. The *Niagara's* long-delayed thunder erupted. From both enemy vessels came an agonized chorus of shrieking, and the *Detroit's* heavy, blunt bows splintered.

Making up for their enforced idleness, the *Niagara's* gunners rapidly served their pieces, and the carronades belched in terrifying, stepped-up salvos that came faster and faster.

Suddenly Perry bellowed an order.

Aboard the *Lady Prevost* he saw only one living man. He was an epauletted officer, apparently her commander and, as he stood bareheaded in the blazing sunlight, blood streaming down his face, he stared vacantly and without recognition at the *Niagara*.

With a twinge of pity, Perry recognized that the *Lady Prevost* was a beaten ship commanded by a senseless man. "Cease firing to larboard! Cease firing *all* larboard batteries and *all* sharpshooters." More punishment to the *Lady Prevost* would be only murder.

On the *Detroit* and *Queen Charlotte* many of the guns, apparently dismounted, had fallen silent, and Perry directed all of his fresh, terrible power against them in concentrated fury.

"Luff up to take positions athwart the *Detroit* and *Queen*," he shouted. "Fire when ready!"

As topmen adjusted sail and yardmen briskly set the yards, the *Niagara* responded smartly. She had suffered only minor damage to rigging and sail, all her guns were yet mounted, breechings sound, carriages working.

Now her broadsides almost pulverized the dying ships, her carronades bowling enemy guns from their mounts, ripping braces, shredding sail and rigging. The inside bulwarks of both ran a deeper, stickier crimson than they had been painted, and the blood slopped in their scuppers.

"Faster!" Perry roared. Victory was very close now. "Fire faster!"

As the double-shotted salvos again were stepped up, the *Queen Charlotte* seemed to sag and suddenly the last of her guns fell silent. An officer appeared on her taffrail, hastily affixed a white cloth to a boarding pike and waved it.

"Free trade and sailors' rights!" The cry rose from the *Niagara's* blackened, sweat-stained tars. "Don't give up the ship!" shouted the gun crews.

But the triumph was momentary. "The *Detroit* ain't struck yet!" bawled a carronade chief. "Fire faster!"

To Perry, the ship seemed almost as dead as the *Queen Charlotte:* every brace gone, mizzen topmast and gaff down, hull shattered, most of her guns overturned or tilted awkwardly. He called for the coup de grâce.

"All hands wear ship. Bear away sharply now, and bring your other broadside into action!"

Almost as he spoke, an officer stepped up to the bulwarks of the ruined *Detroit*, speaking trumpet in hand. Hastily Perry ordered all the guns to cease fire, and the sudden silence came as a shock to ears still ringing with the battle sounds.

"Ahoy the commander aboard!"

"Ahoy," Perry said, moving to the *Niagara's* bulwarks. His own voice sounded strange to him.

"We are striking, sir. I am Lieutenant Inglis of His Majesty's Ship *Detroit*. Captain Richard Barclay, our commander, is below with grave wounds, and I am standing for him."

"Very well, sir. Is this by his order?"

"Aye, aye, sir. We brought him on deck, and he told us to strike."

"Disarm your men and petty officers, sir. Stand by to receive boarders. I shall inform you of the time and place for formal surrender later."

Correctly Perry waited as the British lieutenant saluted and moved away from the bulwark. He lifted his eyes to the Union Jack, never shifting his gaze till the flag came down the enemy halyard.

All at once, though little bits and pieces of the action were still continuing, he felt an enormous relief and weariness and gratitude. "Thanks be to God," he said humbly, then forced himself to supervise the mopping-up operations. He was a tidy man.

CHAPTER 10

IT WAS over. Somewhere overhead a gull shrieked, and Perry started. Though the battle had lasted less than a day, it seemed years since he had heard the peaceful, familiar call of a bird.

Besides the *Detroit*, the *Queen Charlotte* and the *Lady Prevost*, the brig *Hunter* had hauled down her colors, and only the schooner *Chippewa* and sloop *Little Belt* were trying to run for it. With the *Scorpion* and *Trippe* in close pursuit, he dismissed them from his mind as already captured.

Unexpectedly a gun boomed, and he turned to the rail, frowning. Then he grinned broadly. It was the *Scorpion* warning the two fugitives. Steve Champlin, his cousin, had fired the first American shot that day, and now, most appropriately, he had fired the last.

"Lower away a boat and provide for oarsmen," Perry instructed the boatswain. "I'm returning to the *Lawrence*."

"Small boat approaching the larboard gangway," the boatswain said. "Would that one do, sir?"

Perry nodded. It was Elliott returning at last from his superflous errand. He looked ill.

"Think I'll turn in sir. Ill I am. I have lost the fairest opportunity of distinguishing myself that man ever had."

Now that the day had been secured, Perry could almost feel pity, as well as contempt. However he scored Elliott in his official report, it would not repair the damage already done—only tarnish the unique luster of the victory. It was, Perry knew, the first surrender of a British squadron, and he wanted to preserve that shining fact, without cloud or recrimination, for the Navy he loved.

"I do not understand what you are saying, sir," he said shortly.

"Thank you, sir," The shamed Elliott moved slowly toward his cabin.

Perry ordered the *Niagara's* signal officer to make the signal to anchor. For the sake of the wounded, they would rest here overnight, he had decided. Tomorrow would be time enough to return to Put in Bay.

"Small boat's ready, sir," the boatswain sang out.

"Hold her. I have more pressing business first."

As the *Niagara's* heavy anchor dropped and her chain measured the depth, he fished in his pockets for the stub of an old pencil and a soiled, creased official envelope. He had to get off an immediate message to General Harrison.

Beckoning to a sailor, he said, "Your hat, lad." Perry smoothed the envelope on the stiff-topped hat and squinted thoughtfully. How to phrase it? Slowly, with clipped military phrases, he wrote:

> Dear General:
> We have met the enemy and they are ours. Two ships, two brigs, one schooner and one sloop.
> Yours with great respect and esteem,
>
> O. H. Perry

Next, he decided, he must also report to the Secretary of the Navy, and he found a carronade that had cooled sufficiently to be used as a writing desk. On fresh paper he wrote:

> U. S. Brig *Niagara*, off the Western Sister, Head of Lake Erie, September 10, 1813, 4 P.M.
> Sir—It has pleased the Almighty to give to the arms of the United States a signal victory over their enemies on this lake. The British squadron, consisting of two ships, two brigs, one schooner and one sloop have this moment surrendered to the forces under my command after a sharp conflict.
> I have the honor to be, sir, very respectfully, your obedient servant,
>
> O. H. Perry

For the first time, he thought of himself. His uniform was powder-black and sweat-stained, but there wasn't so much as a splinter in it. Feeling himself carefully, he couldn't find a bruise. Elna's prayers have been answered. I must get word to her before she hears of the battle.

The boatswain was still standing by, waiting the commodore's pleasure.

"Send messengers to each of the ships and advise the officers to assemble on the *Lawrence*. I am returning to her now."

As the boatswain's whistle shrilled imperiously, Perry went over the side, climbing carefully down to the small boat. With an enormous yawn, young Jimmy followed. Like a puppy, Perry thought, affectionately. Hasn't learned to pace himself.

Maybe, he thought, the *Lawrence* could be sailed tomorrow if some re-rigging was done overnight. But when he boarded her, he found the damage even worse than he remembered.

Yarnall, Forrest, Doc Parsons stood by to greet him. He missed one face, and asked sharply, "Sam Hambleton?"

"Aft, sir," Yarnall said. "He's been hit. Painful, I reckon, but not serious."

Doc Parsons nodded confirmation. Perry hurried aft to the impromptu hospital the surgeon had rigged, pads on the deck, canvas canopy above to protect the wounded from the sun.

"Hung Elliott yet?" Sam demanded by way of greeting.

"Now, Sam, don't strain your main braces. I hesitate to ruin an officer's career because of one mistake or start a controversy that can only hurt the Navy."

"Mistake!" Sam half-rose, then settled back, grimacing in pain. "Great shiverin' gallowumpies, sir. He was making away!"

"Stop talking, Sam. This is my problem. You've got to rest."

Sam nodded grouchily. "Your packet's on your desk. Told you I'd be returning it."

The cabin, Perry found as he retrieved the packet, was a shambles. A round shot had gone through the closet, smashing every piece of china and strewing the fragments in every direction. His desk was splintered, and the acrid smell of powder hung heavily in the air.

Going aft, he found Dulaney Forrest in charge of a cleanup detail, and called him aside.

"You are from the District of Columbia, I believe, Mr. Forrest? I want you to take this message to Secretary Jones. You will know the quickest way of getting there. And, en route, leave this second message for General Harrison."

"I'll leave immediately, sir."

Perry raised his hand. "Not so fast, Mr. Forrest. Wait for the enemy's flags, mister. I want you to take them to headquarters. And also my blue battle flag."

"Very well, sir. And, beg pardon, sir?"

"Yes?"

"What will the Commodore be doing about Captain Elliott, sir?"

Again Elliott! Perry felt anger rising in him, but restrained himself.

After all, anyone who had served that day on the *Lawrence* had the right to ask the question.

"I understand your feelings, Mr. Forrest. I might say that I sympathize with them. But the honor and future of the Navy which we have the honor to serve are more important than any officer's feelings. Mark that, Mr. Forrest. For that reason, for the present at least, I intend to forget Mr. Elliott."

"Aye, sir. But supposing they had beaten the *Niagara*?"

"Why, then I would have gone back to the next ship," Perry said. "And then, if necessary, to the next and the next till we won or ran out of vessels."

"That's what I told the men when you left us, sir," Forrest said with satisfaction. "I told them the *Lawrence* was only the beginning of the fight."

A short time later, limping painfully, Sam Hambleton sought Perry. It was important, he thought, to report that all the surviving American officers who had come aboard in response to Perry's order were grumbling about Elliott.

"Aye, and the men, even the seriously wounded," added Doc Parsons.

"If you don't bring charges," Sam persisted, "Elliott will get an equal share of the prize money. That's not fair to you, and it's not fair to the other officers. That's one thing that's buggering them."

"Money!" Perry said contemptuously. "I didn't fight for money."

"Then honor! Elliott was making away, and you know it. I challenge your right to hide that fact, sir!"

Perry spoke sharply. "That will be enough, Sam! The decision must be mine."

"Can't stop the scuttlebutt among the men, though," Doc Parsons intervened mildly. "Even a commodore can't. They'll be writing home about Elliott, and talking, and the word will be all over General Harrison's camp, too."

Perry's forehead wrinkled unhappily. "We've got to stop them somehow! Gentlemen, I *love* this Navy. There are those who don't, many of them in high places. Don't you understand!"

"You have no right, sir, to make others share in the dishonor of one," Sam said stubbornly.

"Dammit, bring charges and what happens! Board of inquiry and court-martials! Inspectors from Washington grubbing for anything discreditable against any of us! Pesky Congressmen threatening to cut appropriations! Newspaper editors stirring up controversy!" Perry's voice almost broke. "And then all that we achieved—not for ourselves but for the United States and our Navy—becomes a mess of stinking political garbage. I won't have it! I won't!"

Sam and the ship's surgeon were startled by the outburst. There was an awkward silence, broken a minute later by the appearance of Yarnall. The enemy officers had come alongside, and would Commodore Perry appear on the quarter-deck, please?

Glad of the excuse, Perry accompanied Yarnall to the deck. "See that they are piped aboard, sir, and are given every courtesy," he told his first officer.

The ceremony was brief. Perry declined each sword, as it was offered to him. He inquired solicitously after Captain Barclay and expressed regret at not having any medical officers to spare.

In a tired voice he explained that the American fleet would conduct twilight services for its dead, and suggested that the British do the same. The American officers who had fallen, he went on, would be buried in the morning on South Bass Island. If it were desired, the British officers could be buried there, too.

In behalf of the wounded Barclay, Lieutenant Inglis expressed appreciation of the offer.

"May we use our own flag, sir?"

"Of course." Perry spoke vigorously now. "Of course. You honored your colors today, sir."

He gave Inglis' party instructions for the disposition of their men and ships and saw that they were properly escorted back to their small boats. Then he dropped in exhaustion on an arms chest.

"You don' look right, suh."

"It's the fever, Hannibal. One day it will be the death of me."

"I'll get the tea, suh."

"Not now. First, fetch a meal for my officers, Hannibal."

Wearily he turned to Forrest. "Double rations of grog for the men, mister, if the casks haven't been broached."

"I've taken that liberty, sir."

"Good. It had slipped my mind. And see that they are fed."

"That has also been done, sir."

Forrest hesitated nervously.

"Something wrong, mister?"

"It was something I heard one of the British officers saying, sir. Would it be impertinence, merely to repeat it, sir?"

"Out with it."

Forrest carefully avoided his commander's steely gaze. "He said, sir, that if Captain Elliott had acted as he did under British colors, he would have been hung on the spot!"

"That subject is closed, Mr. Forrest," Perry said. "I would find it most distressing if you ever raise it again in my presence. Now kindly find young Jimmy for me."

Reddening under the rebuke, Forrest disappeared. Perry could hear him calling, "Mr. Perry, lay up to the quarter-deck." There was no answer, and Perry felt sudden anxiety. In confusion like this, anything could happen to a shaver, and he wouldn't even be missed for hours.

But then, as Forrest returned grinning, he relaxed. "Asleep in his berth, sir. Plumb exhausted, I guess."

"Aye, still a puppy."

Slowly, obviously fighting off fatigue himself, Yarnall now reported to the quarter-deck.

"British working party ready to come aboard, sir."

"Marine guard with them?"

"Aye, sir. Six Kentucky sharpshooters."

Perry smiled. "One of those lads would be enough. Bring them aboard, Mr. Yarnall. Have them clean the crew's quarters and wardroom first. The wounded there need good air and clean surroundings. The others need rest."

"Aye, aye, sir."

"And, Mr. Yarnall, thank each man for me. I shall do so in time, but there is much to do. I must see Barclay. They tell me he is hard hit, mister."

His voice softened. "And see that the dead are looked after kindly, sir. Later I shall want to conduct the services myself."

The small boat that was to take Perry to the *Detroit* came alongside. Just as he was preparing to go over the starboard gangway, Yarnall returned. "British officer in charge of the prisoner work detail wishes to speak with the Commodore, sir."

"Oh, dammit, what does he want, mister?" Perry spoke impatiently. He was tired and there was still so much to do, and the fever was hammering at his temples.

"It's about the preparation of the dead, sir."

"We sew dead seamen in their hammocks with a round shot at their feet. Surely the British do the same!"

Yarnall looked uncomfortable. Perry quickly regretted his sharpness. Poor Yarnall had gone through more than he during the day.

"Sorry, Mr. Yarnall. Fetch the Britisher to me."

Perry recognized the haughty young officer as one of the group whose sword he had refused to accept. But he wasn't wearing it now, to his obvious discomfiture. Barclay probably had ordered all officers to remove the weapons, Perry guessed.

"Well, mister?"

"It's about the dead, sir. Should we prepare the blacks the same as the whites, sir?"

Perry was genuinely surprised. "Of course, mister! It is to be a common service. Didn't you understand that?"

"And the savages?" the officer continued almost sulkily.

"Aye." He couldn't resist the hit. "After all, sir, I understand that Tecumseh is a brigadier in His Majesty's service."

The officer flushed angrily, but persisted. "Colored men given the same attention as the whites, sir?"

Arrogant popinjay, Perry swore under his breath. He'd better be given a lesson.

"I tell you what," he said with deceptive helpfulness, "if you feel that some distinction must be made, wash the white blood to the starboard and the colored blood to the larboard, mister. Tell your men to do that."

"You know that they can't tell any difference, sir," the young officer protested.

"Ah," said Perry, "but *you* can, mister. Now *you* go and show them which is which."

Abruptly he turned and went over the port gangway into the waiting small boat.

There was another side to the coin of battle, and two days later at Put in Bay, in the hulk of his flagship, Captain Robert Heriott Barclay, R.N., studied it sadly. From his bunk, in halting tones, he was dictating to Lieutenant Inglis the report he had to make to Sir James Yeo.

"How do we start, sir?"

"Upper right of the page, put 'H.M.'s late ship *Detroit*,' " Barclay said. He paused, collecting his thoughts, then went on to explain how necessity had forced him to leave the protection of Malden. The weak voice droned on.

". . . . and it now remains to me, the most melancholy task, to relate to you the unfortunate issue of the battle, as well as the many untoward circumstances which led to that event."

Candidly he described how the action had gone against him, not sparing himself the memory of Perry's brilliant escape from the dying *Lawrence* to the *Niagara*.

"The action continued with great fury until half-past 2 when I perceived my opponent drop astern, and a boat passing from him to the *Niagara* (which vessel was at this time perfectly fresh); the American Commodore, seeing that as yet the day was against him . . . made a noble, and alas!, too successful an effort to regain it . . ."

The voice trailed into silence. "You're overtired, sir. Tomorrow we can finish."

"No, Inglis, only a little more. We must tell Sir James how well officers and men fought. Even Hoffmeister, a purser, on deck and fighting and badly wounded!"

Slowly he itemized the day's gallantry, name by name, paused again to rest and think for a few minutes. "Here is the end of it, Inglis."

The frail voice resumed. "Captain Perry has behaved in a most humane and attentive manner, not only to myself and officers, but to all the wounded.

"I trust, that although unsuccessful, you will approve of the motives that induced me to sail under so many disadvantages, and that it may be hereafter proved that, under such circumstances, the honor of His Majesty's flag has not been tarnished.

"I enclose the list of killed and wounded."

CHAPTER **11**

As FAST as the news could be carried by post horse, Oliver Hazard Perry became a hero in every American village and city, except possibly back home in Rhode Island. His victory gave the Yankees undisputed supremacy on Lake Erie and through the whole Niagara territory. Best of all, he had released the great Northwest Territory from the threat of tomahawk and scalping knife, and more than one pioneer orator in buckskins thundered to little backwoods audiences: "Erie is the greatest victory in this country since Cornwallis surrendered at Yorktown!"

Throughout the East, a dozen hero's receptions were quickly arranged, but Perry, preferring to help General Harrison with his victory push, politely begged off. As to Rhode Island's curious reaction, the word came first to Jimmy in a letter from home, and the twelve-year-old didn't know what to make of it.

Doubtfully he showed the letter to his older brother and, as Perry read, he smiled, then laughed till the tears came to his eyes. Yarnall, never having seen his commander in such hilarious spirits, was taken aback.

"Excuse me, Mr. Yarnall, but since you haven't met my most distinguished and strong-willed mother, I am afraid you will not quite appreciate the jest. Back home, where she is most widely known and respected, you know what the farmers are saying? They are calling Erie not Perry's victory—but 'Mrs. Perry's victory'!"

Again he roared and, hesitantly, Jimmy joined in the laughter.

"You're not displeased, sir?" he ventured.

"Displeased, lad! Be proud you have such a mother."

In the mood of jubilance that now swept fleet and army alike, Perry was more than ever determined to bury the Elliott scandal. What possible good could come to military and national morale by ugly charges of cowardice and insubordination?

Though he tartly commanded his subordinates to refrain from talking, the gossip reached far beyond the fleet and the nearby campfires of Harrison's army. In fact, Elliott's brother, returning from a trip to the interior of the country, told the captain that many dark stories about him were spreading through the countryside.

In turn, Elliott appealed by letter to Perry, and the Commodore reacted decisively. Both in his official report and in an answer to Elliott's plea, he exonerated him. Perhaps I acted a bit too decisively, Perry later speculated ruefully. Without reservation, he had expressed his indignation over the rumors and he winced as he recalled that, in writing, he had blessed Elliott's conduct with "my warmest approbation."

Then, in the complexities of transporting Harrison's army from the rendezvous on Middle Sister Island to Malden, he forgot the sorry

86

business. There were some 3,500 troops to be moved, and Perry used all of 16 armed vessels and 100 boats to execute the maneuver.

The advancing fleet and army found Malden, along with Detroit, already evacuated. The British had been forced to retreat so hastily that they had fired numerous military storehouses, and to a veteran campaigner like Harrison, the smoking ruins were a good omen. Immediately he dispatched scouts to locate the fleeing army.

General Proctor, they found, was using Lake Saint Clair and the Thames River, a broad, sluggish stream that emptied into the lake, as a water escape route for his baggage and supplies. Trying to head him off, Perry dispatched Elliott in the *Niagara*, along with the captured *Lady Prevost*, the *Scorpion* and the *Tigress*, to the lake. He followed a day later with the *Ariel* and the *Caledonia*.

But Proctor had already reached the Thames by the time Elliott got to the river's mouth. So, with a large number of small gunboats, Perry sent his second-in-command upriver to convoy baggage and protect the passage of the American troops over the Thames. Again he followed, finding the little armada stalled some four miles below the farmhouse of one Isaac Dolsen.

Irritably Perry studied the obstacles. The river narrowed sharply, presenting a series of rapids, swift, white water and high, heavily wooded banks. Nothing to do but leave the boats and baggage under infantry guard, he acknowledged.

Even as he was making his decision, he heard the crackle of musket fire ahead. The pursuers were so close that Harrison's van was skirmishing with Indians up at Chatham, and the big Virginian said he was hoping that maybe on the morrow he could make the English turn and fight.

Impulsively Perry saluted the general. "Sir, I'd like to volunteer as aide-de-camp to the general."

"What!" exclaimed Harrison, surprised but obviously pleased. "Take orders from a landlubber, Commodore?"

"Aye—I mean, yes, sir."

"Chambers!" the general rumbled. Major John Chambers, the tall, Jersey-born Kentucky lawyer who had volunteered to serve as Harrison's aide, came up.

"Competition for you, John. The Commodore here has just nominated himself as my aide."

"Delighted, sir," Chambers said warmly. "We're honored and, more practically, we need a water expert in this campaign."

"Get him a horse, Chambers. Preferably a frisky one, sir. Shake him up a little the way he treats us in those damned boats of his. God, sir, my belly's still turning over."

Early next morning, dubiously mounting the nag that Chambers had found for him, Perry rode slowly and awkwardly alongside the general. He envied the old campaigner's slouching, relaxed carriage. It was as though he were sitting in a rocking chair. Perry felt his horse might rear, fore or aft, any minute and he kept a tense hand on the reins.

For more than three hours they moved through a lush farm country deeply colored with the rich, golden tans of the harvest season, and yet not once did Perry see a farmer, or even a child. The land seemed deserted.

Carefully placing one weathered hand on his mount's rump, he half-turned in the saddle to look at the foot soldiers who slogged along behind as easily as Harrison rode.

All above average height, all bearded, they carried their long rifles as though the heavy weapons were part of them. They weren't a spit-and-polish army, by far. Many were chewing tobacco, there was uninhibited fraternizing among them, and every so often, one or another would loose a wolflike, eerie cry.

"Remember the River Raisin!"

Then the others would take up the cry, and even a hardened military man like Perry felt a tingle of dismay at the naked ferocity in their voices.

"Know the story?" Harrison asked.

Perry nodded. Ten months earlier, General James Winchester had successfully but rashly moved against Frenchtown (later Monroe), Michigan. There Proctor had surprised him, and the Americans surrendered with the understanding they would be protected from the barbarism of the Britishers' Indian allies.

Instead, the savages were allowed to run amok and, in all, of an army of about one thousand, the American loss was more than nine hundred, mostly Kentuckians.

"Bestial brute," Harrison growled. "Proctor could have saved the prisoners. Instead, he let the Indians burn them in their prison cabins and scalp and tomahawk as they pleased. Then he even commended the Indians for their 'bravery'!"

"No wonder the countryside is deserted!" Perry exclaimed. "These

88

people must be really frightened, figuring we too would commit all kinds of atrocities."

Though he studied each substantial farmhouse as they passed, there were no signs of life. All had fled before the advance of the Americans.

"Most likely, the poor devils take brutalities for granted," the general said. "If the British and Indians have treated them badly, what could they expect from us."

"Aye," Perry said. "It's the people on the land who are always hurt in such wars."

Again the wolflike howl rose behind them. "Remember the River Raisin!"

Perry turned toward the big slouching figure alongside. "These are the people who came as pioneers and now stand to lose all their years of labor to fire and sword. Surely we won't find it necessary to hurt them?"

Harrison sighed ponderously. "My Kentuckians aren't easy to hold. But I've warned 'em, and warned 'em again, that anyone who touches a stick to one of these farms answers direct to me."

Two scouts, their fringed jackets soaking wet, trotted easily down the road toward Harrison's party. The general reined his mount to a halt, and Perry did the same.

With a casual gesture that might have been a salute, the frontiersmen reported. "Wal, I'll be dogged!" exclaimed the taller of the pair, recognizing Perry. "Awful nice to see you, Commodore! My brother who was with ya says everythin' good and nothin' bad about ya!"

"That's enough for now, Jeb," Harrison said easily as Perry flushed in embarrassment. "What's the report?"

Jeb was not to be hurried. "Got wet a-crawlin' through dew grass up ahaid and tryin' out the ford at Arnold's Mill."

"Well, man, let's have it."

Ignoring the interruption, Jeb went on with the report in his own manner.

"Left my powder on the bank. Ferd here covered me whilst I tried it out. Too blamed deep for foot troops, sir. Wouldn't be a dry grain o' powder left in camp."

Harrison, sighing in relief that they were now getting to the point, asked whether there might be fighting soon now.

"I calc'late so," Jeb drawled. "Ole Proctor's gonna have to turn and fight pretty quick now. Them Injuns is a willawallin' somethin' fierce. Gettin' purty tired o' running, I reckon."

"We're really getting closer then?" Perry interjected.

"Yes, sir," Ferd answered. "Some o' the boys got a couple more o' them little gunboats. That were the shootin' ye heerd a whilst ago."

"Why didn't you send back for help?" the general asked.

"Let a whole durn gang in on it, sir?" Ferd asked in a scandalized tone. "Weren't necessary at all."

The scouts had found the British regulars on Harrison's right, they reported, straddling the road. Tecumseh's Indians and others under Oshawahnah were on the Americans' center and left. When Harrison asked the distance, the scouts eyed each other, kicked thoughtfully at the ground with their moccasined feet and squinted in thought.

"I'd calc'late we was maybe two musket shots, sir," Jeb finally said.

Ferd nodded solemnly in agreement. "Maybe three to ole Proctor hisself."

Harrison's shaggy eyebrows lifted in disbelief.

"Figger we got an earlier start than they did this mornin'," Jeb explained. "Heard tell ole Proctor fancies up his breakfast grub."

Harrison, nodding, asked about the Indians.

"Just ahead," Ferd reported. " 'Course the varmints is a-sneakin' around jes out in front all the time."

"More blamed bird calls thet ain't bird calls out thar than ye can shake a stick at," Jeb amplified. "Maybe a pistol shot ahead. No, Ferd?"

"Yes, Jeb."

In their leisurely way the pair further related that, having been able to sneak close as Proctor pulled out in the morning, they had got a look at his heavy weapons. About 20 twenty-four-pounders, they estimated.

"When the fight comes, we've got to do something quick about those cannon," Harrison said. "Knock them out fast or overrun them."

As a naval man, Perry was more interested in the deep water at Arnold's Mill.

"Gonna' have do suthin'," big Jeb said in aggrieved tones.

"Besides gettin' your powder wet, it ain't good a-walkin' in wet britches, anyways."

Perry questioned the pair closely to make sure the Americans could not be ambushed while crossing at the mill. But Ferd and Jeb explained there was no cover for the enemy for several hundred yards on their side of the river.

"If they was to try anythin' like thet, we'd shoot 'em to doll rags from this side with our long rifles," Jeb said. It wasn't boasting, Perry recognized, just simple statement of fact, and he had the comforting feeling that these odd Kentuckians spoke only what they knew they could do.

As Harrison's "water expert," he suggested the best maneuver would be for the cavalry to ferry the foot troops across the ford. The general nodded and asked him to supervise the operation.

As Perry spurred ahead somewhat uncertainly on his nag, he drew shouts and cheers from the bearded Kentuckians in the van.

"Hey, Commodore! How's about shippin' across on one o' yer big boats!"

"Hurrah fer Admiral Perry!" shouted another. "Free trade and sailor's rights! Don't give up the land, neither!"

The rough, outspoken admiration was embarrassing, and Perry spurred his mount to get to the ford as quickly as possible. There he was joined by Major Chambers and Captain Charles Scott Todd, another of Harrison's aides. The son of a United States Supreme Court Justice, Todd was, like Chambers, a Kentucky lawyer, and so gifted that later he was to serve as the American minister to Saint Petersburg.

Now, with the felicity of a diplomat, he greeted Perry. "If admiration was gunpowder, sir," he said, laughingly, "You'd have enough here to blow up the world."

"It warms me, sir," Perry confessed, "but I don't understand it. "Your fellow Kentuckians all seem to know me, and they even bring me choice tidbits."

"In many ways they're like boys—impish, mischievous, full of the Old Nick," explained Captain Todd. "But when it comes to walking forty miles a day or firing those long rifles, they're men's men. And when they like a commander, they let him know it."

Perry nodded in amusement. He walked closer to the water, studying the broad fording spot. "How deep?" he asked one of the soldiers.

" 'Bout six feet, I reckon."

"What about the cavalry taking you foot men across?"

"They say the horses is tired, suh." The bearded frontiersman thoughtfully scratched himself. "They ain't so fair happy at the thought of it."

Well, Perry thought, we'll have to try it.

"Follow me, and keep 'em moving," he told Captain Todd. "Let's put on a full press of canvas."

Perry extended a hand to a Kentucky foot soldier. "Come aboard, lad." The frontiersman looked startled, then grinned and swung lithely astraddle the horse's rump, clutching Perry's waist.

"All right, you men on horseback, look lively now!" Perry's voice had the sting of quarter-deck authority. "Each of you, take a man aboard and ferry him across."

The cavalrymen seemed hesitant. "Remember River Raisin!"

The slogan worked. Weary cavalrymen swung into action, and, as Perry spurred his mount into the stream, the others followed. Behind, there was a sudden burst of cheering, and Perry felt his passenger squirming to look back.

"What's going on aft?" he asked.

"Genr'l Harrison, sir. He's a-takin' one o' the boys aboard, too. Skinny fellow, which is lucky for the genr'l's horse."

On the far bank Todd and Chambers told Perry they would press ahead with the vanguard forces, and Perry decided to go along, too.

About eight miles further on, they reached the spot where Proctor had bivouacked the previous night.

Kneeling to feel the ashes of the campfire, a Kentuckian found them still hot. "We're gettin' mighty nigh thar, I reckon," he said.

It was a good place, they decided, to wait for Harrison. Cavalrymen dismounted, tethered their horses and sprawled on the ground.

Todd tried to bring up the subject of Elliott's behavior. "It's none of my business, sir. But if half of what your men say is true, I'd have shot him!"

Perry shook his head firmly. "I'd really rather not discuss it," he said. With a diplomat's born tact, the captain dropped the subject, and there was silence until Harrison arrived with the rest of his headquarters party.

He talked a few moments with a scout who had just returned from the front, then dismounted and, leading his horse, joined Perry, Chambers and Todd.

"We fight today!" he rumbled. Nodding toward Todd, he ordered, "Pass the word to all commanders. Have the men check their pieces for fouling. Move the artillery forward. It isn't going to be long now!"

Within fifteen minutes, they heard the abrupt crackle of musketry. Almost immediately, runners came back from the forces of Colonel Richard M. Johnson. Johnson had been halted by heavy firing from cover, and wanted to know General Harrison's wishes.

Old Tippecanoe said he would walk forward to look things over.

CHAPTER 12

AT THE age of thirty-two, Richard Mentor Johnson, a highly successful lawyer-politician, had already served in the state legislature and gone on to Washington as a congressman. With a talent for public affairs, he was later to serve as a United States Senator and a Vice-President of the United States. Except for two factors, there seemed to be absolutely no reason for him to risk his life in active warfare.

In the first place, having voted for the War of 1812 as a congressman, he felt, with simple logic, that it was a public duty to back up his ballot with bullets. But, far more important, he was Kentucky-born, son of a pioneer who had fought the Indians, and he would have been heartbroken to miss a part in the battle.

Now, with the thousand mounted volunteers he had raised in his home state, with his brother James as his lieutenant colonel, he was Harrison's spearhead. And spoiling to fight, Perry thought, as he listened to Johnson describe the enemy's deployment.

Proctor, apparently resigned that he could run no longer, was halted in front of a Moravian settlement about a mile and a half beyond the Americans. He had chosen his position wisely, Johnson conceded.

On the left, Proctor had anchored his line to the broad Thames River and on the right to an impassable swamp. His regulars and Indians were drawn up directly across Harrison's line of march. At a point where the road ran close alongside the river, he had concentrated his cannon. Tecumseh's forces were deployed on his right.

Harrison studied the terrain between the two armies. The ground was firm, but there was very little underbrush, and a thick forest of beeches made maneuvering difficult. Because of the cramped space, he could commit only half his men, and he knew he could win just one way—by a lightning-hard smash that gave the enemy no time for regrouping.

As he was making his deployments, a scout trotted into the command post, breathing heavily. "Beg pardon, sir," he gasped. "There's somethin' funny the way them British is set out thar."

"Damn it, soldier, don't interrupt the general!" Johnson barked.

93

Harrison silenced him. "What do you mean, lad?"

"Wal, sir, they ain't a-waitin' in close order, like usual, but they's in open skirmish formation."

"Ah!" Harrison exclaimed. "As you were on that deployment, gentlemen! This changes the situation."

The others waited respectfully as Old Tippecanoe pondered a new attack. "By George, I have it!" he said suddenly. "I'll use the cavalry up front. We'll bowl them over!"

Colonel Chambers looked dismayed. "Our Kentucky boys ride like devils and handle muskets well from horseback. But it's unorthodox as hell, sir."

"Exactly! They won't be looking for a mounted regiment in the assault. We'll break through the open skirmish formation and get at their rear. Then we'll pin Proctor's whole outfit between the cavalry and the foot troops."

Harrison ordered Johnson and Colonel Whitley, commander of a particularly tough band of sixty advance scouts known as the "Forlorn Hope," to form the mounted battalions. Perry, he said, could help them. Meanwhile, his other two aides, Major Chambers and Captain Todd, would be busy carrying the general's orders to the infantry commanders. Later, if there was time, they could rejoin Perry for the charge.

Heavily, Harrison got on his mount, swinging about to face Perry. "You understand, Commodore, that fighting in a forest is somewhat different than fighting at sea?" There was a note of concern in his voice.

"Not much so far as strategy is concerned, sir. We put up our helm and bear down sharply under full canvas to break the enemy line and rake them fore and aft."

"Aye," said Harrison, using Perry's familiar expression. "Don't give up the ship, sir!"

He wheeled his big mount and trotted briskly toward his command post on the main road near the river. Johnson filled in Perry on the details.

His brother, he explained, was leading the right battalion where the enemy cannon straddled the road close to the river. Johnson planned to swing left by the small swamp to flush out Tecumseh's Indians, while reinforcements covered him to prevent flanking or infiltration. If all went well, the infantry would follow, cleaning up any pockets of holdouts.

"Some special orders for me, sir?" Perry asked hopefully.

"You know something about big guns, Commodore. I'd appreciate your keeping a weather eye on their artillery at the extreme right. If we can take that, we take their biggest persuader."

"Aye, aye, sir." Perry galloped his mount toward the right.

With an approving professional eye he noted that the lines were efficiently formed in twenty minutes, despite the deceptively casual movements of the Kentuckians. Runners darted from one command post to the next, relaying orders. Then there was the hush that precedes battle.

Suddenly a bugle blared, then a few quick shots followed.

Next, Perry heard the sustained crackle of musketry, which increased in volume, and a new sound, almost a shriek, that rose to the tops of the beeches.

"Remember the River Raisin! Remember the Raisin!"

The Kentuckians charged.

From the massed enemy cannon, thunderous salvos ripped into the mounted lines. Suddenly Perry saw the rider just ahead of him rear stiffly in the saddle, his head torn off by canister. Then the body toppled, and the frightened horse reared and plunged aimlessly, dragging the headless corpse by one foot.

Under the deluge of well-aimed metal, the entire mounted line began recoiling. Horses milled in confusion, and casualties on the ground screamed as they were kicked and trodden by the heavy hoofs.

Perry drew his sword and, whirling it overhead, roared new hope into the dazed men.

"At 'em, my hearties! Hit 'em before they can load another broadside! Board them, lads! Board! Get those cannon!"

As he charged the big guns, the shrieking Kentuckians rallied behind, and the mounted line swept forward.

Under the shock of attack, the gunners scurried to cover, and the following line cut them down with rifle and pistol fire. Dismounting, the frontiersmen moved from tree to tree, elusive as Indians, picking off the stragglers. British regulars began throwing down their rifles and raising their hands.

Captain Todd galloped to Perry, shouting exuberantly that 600 regulars of the proud British Forty-First had surrendered. Another 50, who had cut their way out, were retreating under heavy fire.

"How goes it here?"

"We have their big guns" Perry said. "There's no fight left."

All through their sector the firing had died down, but from the swamp Perry and Todd heard sharp musketry.

"Colonel Johnson is tackling Tecumseh's Indians," Todd said. "He and Whitley will show the devils what for!"

Harrison rode up, a smile on his big, plain face. "A complete rout, gentlemen," he announced. "Proctor is broken. We've heard he tossed his baggage into a carriage and is trying to make a run for it. Major Chambers is pursuing with a mounted detail."

Then his face clouded. "But Johnson was hit three times, badly. Dr. Theobald has him back by Dr. Mitchell's stand."

A runner came up with additional casualty figures, and Harrison calculated that the victory had been bought cheap, with only about a dozen fatalities and a score of wounded.

"The savages have lost heart," he said grimly. "They're melting away, and some of the men say that Johnson himself killed Tecumseh."

"Does Johnson confirm it, sir?"

Harrison shook his head. "Unfortunately not. He remembers shoot-one particularly handsome buck who was charging him with a toma-hawk. Shot him right in the face. But he was dressed in plain deerskin like any other Indian."

A young lieutenant hastily rode up to report that some of the Kentuckians were taking scalps. "And a couple of them are flaying a dead chief, sir," he added. "They just growl 'River Raisin' and refuse to stop."

Harrison sighed. "I was afraid this might happen. Go with the lieutenant, Todd, and stop these barbarities at once."

He looked apologetically toward Perry, then spurred his mount toward the Moravian village behind the scene of the battle. On the outskirts the general and Perry found a group of squaws weeping and putting ashes of their faces.

"They throwed their young'uns into the river afore we got here," a bearded soldier explained without much sympathy. "Thought we'd scalp 'em. Now they know we'uns ain't gonna do 'em no harm, and they're real grievin'."

Perry felt almost sick to his stomach. "Did they all drown?" he exclaimed.

"Yep," the soldier said laconically. "Whole passel o' the young'uns laid out on the bank. Them's the ones they got back. Reckon they's lots more they didn't."

Perry and Harrison rode back to the American camp in silence. Always the innocents must suffer in war, Perry thought bitterly, even Indian babies.

There was loud frontier jubilance now among the uninhibited Kentuckians, but Perry couldn't join in. Usually, after battle, he felt a letdown, a nagging Christian guilt at having enjoyed himself, a remorse over the irrevocable bill that had been paid in human life and pain.

Now the fever was acting up again, and Perry desperately wanted to go home to Newport for a rest. He had already applied to Chauncey to be relieved of the Erie command. Chauncey would probably approve and turn the command over to Elliott. That would certainly make both of them happy.

Vaguely he heard Harrison and Todd bantering in loud voices.

"Suppose he's landsick, sir?" the captain inquired.

"No, most probably daydreaming about the wonderful receptions he'll be getting," Harrison boomed. "Torchlight parades, speeches by mayors, cooing by lovely ladies. Ah, captain, for a sailor's life!"

The general nudged him, and Perry started, his face reddening. "My apologies, gentlemen. My mind was miles away, but not on receptions. I dread them."

"Come, sir," Harrison bantered. "The hero of Erie, a foot soldier at Fort George, a cavalryman at Thames! And now you coyly profess to fear friendly forces."

"But what does one say?" Perry asked simply. "I'm not the hero of Erie. The heroes of Erie cannot speak. We buried them on South Bass Island."

Harrison nodded understandingly. "You're tired, Commodore. I know you want to go back to Detroit and then to Put in Bay. So perhaps you will accept the hospitality of my tent to get some rest."

Perry thanked him gratefully and, finding a rough bed in the general's quarters, threw himself down on it without even bothering to remove his shoes. He remembered only one thing before he dropped off into a deep sleep—he must see about getting a parole for Captain Barclay as soon as he got back to Erie.

Half an hour later, Harrison returned to the tent to draft his official report of the battle. He tiptoed to a makeshift plank table and eased himself quietly onto an upended keg.

Then, looking at Perry, he took out paper and pencil and began to write slowly. Halfway down the report he paused, then added:

"My gallant friend, Commodore Perry, accompanied me at the head of the army and assisted me in forming the line of battle; and the appearance of the brave commodore cheered and animated every breast."

CHAPTER 13

HARRISON's victory at Thames River, following so closely on Perry's at Lake Erie, caught the military administrators in Washington by surprise. As a result, the commodore and the general impatiently marked time for two weeks at Detroit waiting for new orders.

As he waited, Perry worried over a letter from Navy Secretary Jones outlining the division of the spoils wrung from the British on Lake Erie. The British prizes had been appraised at $255,000. Congress would soon authorize Presidential purchase of the vessels.

Jones wrote that Chauncey, who had not even been in the same lake, let alone at the battle itself, would receive $12,750. Perry was to get $7,140 and Elliott, whose conduct Perry had somewhat rashly defended, would be awarded a like amount. So far as the money was concerned, Perry sincerely did not care; sometimes prize money seemed like blood money to him.

But he realized, with a sinking feeling, that the money distribution was going to create trouble among his officers. And it did. One by one, they came grumbling to him that Chauncey had euchered him out of the lion's share and that Elliott—well, as one lieutenant put it, Captain Elliott should have been made to pay a spectator's fee, sir." Curtly, Perry reminded his officers that the Elliott business had been settled, once and for all.

It was a relief when the orders finally came through. Perry was to sail for Erie by way of Put in Bay. There he was to pick up the convalescent Barclay, whose parole had been granted, and deposit him at Erie. From the port Barclay would go on to Buffalo and eventually to England.

At the same time Harrison got his instructions. He was to take 2,000 of his best men up to Fort George, and he decided to go with Perry as far as Erie.

A following wind blew freshly. All her fore-and-aft-rigged canvas drawing, the *Ariel* was flying toward Erie.

Near the bow, Perry, on the heaving deck, listened to the crash of the spray as the schooner's forefoot caught and split the waves. He searched the reeling horizon, then turned his face aloft as six bells sounded. It was habit. Day or night, when on deck, he would gaze at sun or stars when the time sounded.

It was an angry-looking day. High wind clouds streaked a somber sky.

Six bells. Managing an approximate fix on the location of the sun, he nodded with satisfaction. He turned and walked slowly aft to watch the wake churn out behind the *Ariel*.

But, part way, he found General Harrison firmly clutching the foremast with both hands, a determined look on his face.

"Standing there in that spray, you'll come down with a chill," Harrison chided him. "By God, sir, there's a bite in the air these days."

Perry grinned. "Nice to see you on deck, General." Perry loosened his faded blue nankeen jacket and shrugged off the moisture. With exaggerated solicitude he asked, "You are beginning to find your balance?"

Harrison ignored the question. "Do you enjoy getting yourself soaked?" he grumbled. "Why don't your lads wet you down with their buckets when they wet the sails to catch the wind?"

Perry laughed. "I enjoy standing in bow-flung spray on such days, sir. It soothes the mind and spirit. . . . My work on Erie is done now. I'll be glad to get home."

"Be going home soon myself," Harrison predicted darkly. "President Madison will find a way to dispense with my services."

Perry started. "Dispense with your services? Hell, General, you've twice whipped the greatest Indian leader the savages had! You're the man for over-all command."

Harrison shook his head. "No. Kind of you, Commodore. But I have a feeling they'll stick me at some dead post to rot. Then I'll get fed up and quit."

The *Ariel* lurched suddenly, and Perry quickly reached out a hand as the general staggered. "This is a nor'wester, with the full sweep of the lake," Perry explained. "But we're making excellent time."

The *Ariel* would anchor only a day or so at Erie, Perry added. They would take on stores and Barclay would have a chance to get some rest.

"How in the hell is he going to get home?" Harrison demanded. "I'm told he hasn't a sou."

"A loan," Perry said. "I'm making the arrangements."

99

Under the general's quizzical stare, Perry reddened. "He took a bad mauling, sir. Hit three times, and almost lost the use of his only arm." Harrison removed his hat and shook his shaggy mane almost angrily. "Damn it, sir, you're too kind to people. Too naïve, too. You know you let Chauncey steal the lion's share of the prize money."

"Erie Harbor bar, ahoy!"

The lookout's warning was a welcome interruption. Perry and Harrison moved over to the rail. Hannibal came up with the tea and, after gingerly taking a few sips, Perry called his sailing master.

"Anchor as close as we can to the foot of French Street," he directed. "I'm taking Captain Barclay to Duncan's Hotel, and I hope to reach there unnoticed. It would be quite painful for him if he had to watch an enthusiastic reception for us."

"Aye, aye, sir." Taylor left to carry out the orders.

"Aye, aye, sir," mimicked Harrison. "That's all your men say! None of them has the gumption to tell you that a reception would do you good."

Perry shrugged, finished the tea and beckoned Hannibal to take away the cup.

Less than half her canvas drawing and more of it being steadily furled, the *Ariel* glided smoothly across the sand bar and down the lee side of the harbor.

Eight bells sounded, and Perry automatically looked aloft. Topmen were furling all sails now, and an anchor dragging its chain to the bottom clattered loudly.

"Noon," he said. "Very good time."

Perry called Taylor and told him to have the gig brought alongside immediately, and to notify Captain Barclay, the naval officer's surgeon and young Jimmy Perry.

"Oarsmen, sir?" Taylor asked.

"Aye. Bring four, including Hannibal, and the small sail. I think we can use the breeze going in."

Taylor moved aft, bawling orders.

Ashore, a distant explosion rumbled, and then another. "Field pieces, I'd say," Harrison remarked. "It's a national salute, sir."

Perry studied the crowd and the transparencies waving in the air, then smiled. "I guess it is, sir."

"A victory such as yours, rescuing this frontier from fear, amply merits public celebration," Harrison said in oracular tones. "You must take your rewards cheerfully, young man."

"But whose army routed Proctor and dispelled the fear that the Indians would cross on the ice and wipe out Erie?" Perry demanded. Through the spyglass he studied one of the transparencies and slowly read out the message:

"General Harrison, fifth of October, 1813."

"Damn," the general said.

"As you so wisely observed a moment ago, sir, the victor must take rewards cheerfully," Perry reminded him.

Harrison laughed resignedly. "Well, we can run the gantlet together."

Slowly, supported by his surgeon, his one arm heavily bandaged and in a sling, Captain Barclay came on deck. It was an awkward moment. Perry and Harrison were silent. For a moment the anguish showed on Barclay's face and then he managed a smile.

"Please, gentlemen, feel no unnecessary delicacy. This is your due."

The skies were clearing and the breeze failing as the gig's bow grated onto the pebbled beach at the foot of French Street. With deafening cheers the crowds surged forward, and Perry leaped lightly ashore.

Harrison followed and then the two, along with the British surgeon, made a protective wedge for Barclay. But the people pressed dangerously close, trying to touch Perry and Harrison, and once Barclay was almost jostled off his feet.

"I admit it's a kind of torment, old man," he said wryly to Perry. "But at least I'm not in chains. I'm being treated as a human being."

It was only a short distance to Duncan's Hotel on French and Third streets, but cheering men and weeping women delayed them almost half an hour. Finally they got Barclay into bed, and the exhausted officer immediately fell asleep.

Returning to the tavern, Perry and Harrison encountered a rousing reception. It was late in the afternoon before they could leave the admiring crowd. Perry went back to Duncan's to make sure young Jimmy was all right, found him asleep in their room and decided on a nap himself.

Slowly he removed his jacket, boots and pants, then padded across the room to look out the window that fronted on Lake Erie. Beyond the bar he saw several sails. Elliott was arriving with the *Niagara* and the rest of the fleet. Might as well get his nap, Perry decided. If he knew Mr. Elliott, the captain would report to him by letter to the *Ariel*, then hastily make for shore, hoping to get a welcoming reception for himself.

It was dark when an insistent rapping roused Perry. "Come in," he said drowsily.

"Though I better be callin' you, sir," Taylor apologized. "It's gettin' a bit late, and there's a letter from Captain Elliott. He sent it to the *Ariel*, and they brought it in for you."

As Taylor lighted candles for him, Perry opened and read the letter. Just as he had thought. Elliott reported himself much indisposed and had decided to come directly ashore to sick quarters. Perry looked inquiringly at Taylor.

"The captain arrived late in the afternoon," Taylor reported. "He seemed somewhat unhappy that the people weren't on hand to greet him." He paused delicately. "Of course, sir, many of the celebrants, having been late at the tavern, were no doubt home and fast asleep at the time."

Perry laughed. "Come, come, no shilly-shallying, Mr. Taylor. What you are trying to say is that the general and I stole the celebration."

"Sir!" Another knock at the door interrupted Taylor's flustered explanation, and Perry nodded to him to open it. Stephen Champlin, Perry's handsome, happy-go-lucky cousin, came in.

"Well, Mr. Champlin, the *Scorpion* has finally arrived!" Perry greeted him. "What kept you? Lose a mast? Or have you forgotten how Rhode Islanders clap on full said in a breeze when less hardy masters keep hove-to under short sail?"

Steve managed a weak grin. "You know me better, sir, I trust. It was Captain Elliott's orders. He sure fills a signal halyard during routine passage."

Perry nodded understandingly.

"Think he really wanted to put in here all by himself," Steve went on. "Now he's sulking because you and General Harrison are getting all the attention."

"Oh, we've been making regular fools of ourselves, you may be sure," Perry said lightly.

"The fever's after him again," Taylor interjected. "He ought to have rested the day instead of giving in to the folks as he did."

Champlin nodded absently, twisting his hat nervously in his hands, and Perry knew something was bothering him. "Out with it, Steve!"

"It's Jesse Elliott, sir. I know how you feel about the subject, but the thing has reached the point where you *must* listen." Champlin's face reddened angrily. "More than that, you've got to act, sir. You've got to, now!"

CHAPTER 14

IRRITABLY Perry sprawled on the lumpy hotel bed to hear Steve Champlin out. If the big devil weren't a blood relative, he thought grumpily, he could pull rank and shut him up. As it was, for family sake, he would have to listen again to the thrice-told tales about Mr. Elliott's behavior during the battle.

But as Steve started pouring out his story, Perry sat up in amazement. "Are you sure of what you're saying, Steve?"

"Aye, sir." Steve's face bore a grim expression. "And I heard the same thing from him before on the Thames when he was quartered on the *Scorpion*. He claims, sir, that the officers and men of the *Lawrence* aren't entitled to prize money because she is a recaptured vessel."

The sheer audacity of it left Perry speechless. Trying to keep his voice from shaking, he asked whether Mr. Elliott had any explanation for his own action aboard the *Niagara*, which had allowed the *Lawrence* to be captured in the first place.

"Aye, sir. He said he had no signal from you to change position."

"That's a——" Perry caught himself. "You know that is not correct, Steve. When I hoisted the battle flag, it was a prearranged signal to lay your designated adversary alongside."

Champlin nodded in agreement, but said that did not change the situation so far as Captain Elliott was concerned. That was why, Steve insisted, Perry would simply have to take some action.

"And there's still one more thing," he added reluctantly. "The man had been wetting his nose when he said it. But, by God, I think you should know it, Ollie, whether he was drunk or sober. He said, '*I only regret that I didn't sacrifice the fleet when it was in my power to do so.*'"

"Steve, that sounds incredible!"

"On my word, Ollie, that's his exact language, and no possible mistake about it."

Perry felt stunned and sick. He looked silently at Champlin and Taylor, whose rough, reddened face mirrored Perry's shock. Elliott, he knew, should be cashiered from the service, but again he found himself in the box he had carpentered. Charges now would cloud the glory of the victory, and there was his own rash letter defending Elliott's conduct.

Harrison was right, he thought bitterly. I'm naïve. Worse, I'm a blithering fool.

A rapping broke the silence, and Old Tippecanoe entered. His face was troubled and his voice abrupt as he addressed Champlin and Taylor.

"If you will excuse me, gentlemen, I would like to speak alone with Commodore Perry on a matter of some urgency."

"Of course, sir," Steve said. Beckoning to Taylor, he rose, and they left the room.

Harrison made sure the door was firmly closed, then turned to Perry, rubbing his nose in embarrassment.

"I don't quite know where to start, Commodore."

"I would suggest with the keel, sir."

"Eh?"

"The beginning."

"Ah, of course. It's about Captain Elliott."

Removing his hat, Harrison carefully adjusted his bulk in a fragile-looking chair and blurted out the story. Elliott had come to him late in the afternoon, complaining that he was being slandered by false rumors about his conduct in the battle. Slowly the general added that Elliott felt these rumors had been inspired by Perry's official report which misled the public.

Perry's head throbbed with a hammering worse than the fever inflicted.

Harrison coughed apologetically. "Please understand my position, Commodore. As you know, I was a friend of Captain Elliott's late father. Only because of that, I agreed to state to you the substance of his complaints."

"Aye, General, I sympathize with your position. And, each day, I begin to understand Mr. Elliott's better and better. What does this insufferable captain want now?"

"Just a meeting with you, Oliver, sometime tomorrow morning. Since we must leave for Buffalo, I told him it would have to be early."

"Surely, sir, a subordinate in the Navy has the privilege of access to his superior without Army intervention," Perry said shortly. "Unless such an interview is entirely out of order—as this one is. I refuse to see him!"

Harrison's big, plain face showed hurt, and Perry quickly added, "I didn't intend that as a rebuke to you, my friend. Forgive me, and let me think a moment."

Carefully Perry considered the possibilities. He must be prudent, he knew.

Elliott must have had a strong motive to capitalize shamelessly on Harrison's loyalty to his dead father. Obviously he was trying to establish for the record that Perry bore him malice. If Perry declined to see him, he could later argue that even a revered figure like General Harrison had been unable to shake the commodore's hostility.

On the other hand, it was grossly insulting to himself and his other officers to expect him to *debate* with Mr. Elliott the contents of an official report. By God, he wouldn't stoop to that! Again he felt the hammering in his temples.

"Do you know, specifically, what part of your report is being challenged?" Harrison asked curiously.

"Quite specifically!"

The evening of the action, Perry explained, he had done Elliott the courtesy of showing him a rough draft of the report. Elliott had agreed to it, but later complained of the manner in which Perry spoke of the *Niagara* and asked if it could be changed.

"I told him I thought not. But I promised to reflect and, if I could do so with propriety, I would alter it. On reflection, general, I was sensible that I had already said and done too much."

"You mean in shielding Captain Elliott and then writing that letter in defense of his conduct?"

"Aye! As someone has said to me, that may well have been the mistake of my life."

"Forgive an old man for intruding, Ollie. But I feel that you must make some decision. Having given Elliott this much rope, you can't rein up sharp now. What shall I tell him?"

Again Perry's mind raced over the alternatives, and then his haggard face dissolved into a mirthless smile. He had it!

Though he insisted on the accuracy of the report, he told Harrison, he would consent to arbitration by two officers. They would examine it to determine whether Perry had done any injustice to Elliott. If so, he would immediately forward the necessary alteration to the Secretary of the Navy and also arranged that the correction receive public circulation.

Harrison pondered, then nodded in agreement. "That's fair enough to both sides, Ollie. And the officers?"

"You may select one of them, sir, and Captain Elliott the other."

"More than fair! But then, sir, I have come to expect that of you." The general's face was troubled. "Again I beg you to understand my delicate position. I trust this mission will not cloud our personal friendship."

Perry smacked Harrison's broad back. "Never, sir!" The hard little smile played at the corners of his mouth. "Matter of fact, I think you are giving me the means to dispose of Mr. Elliott once and for all."

Harrison rose, shaking his head in relief. "I will transmit your decision to Captain Elliott, sir. My own choice, since I know him as a sensible officer and a dependable one, I can give you right now. He is Lieutenant Daniel Turner. I shall inform you as to Elliott's choice."

At the door, he paused. "Forget this miserable business for the time being, Ollie. There's a torchlight parade tonight—for you and me. Let's try to enjoy being heroes."

Perry couldn't dismiss the matter so easily from his mind. Was it possible that he *had* made a mistake? He remembered what he had written when the events were fresh in his mind: At half past two, the wind springing up, "Captain Elliott was enabled to bring his vessel, the *Niagara*, into close action."

Surely that was more than generous! Unless, unless, the thought nagged at him, he had been mistaken as to the time element. He decided to check with Barclay, who surely had nothing to gain or lose by telling the truth.

When he knocked gently outside the captain's hotel room, a reedy voice called, "Come in," and Perry found Barclay propped up in his bed by two pillows. Barclay, he recalled, had asked him immediately after the battle who had been commanding the Niagara, and now he grunted contemptuously at the mention of Elliott's name.

"You've made no mistake, sir," the English officer said decisively. "Your report is correct. It was half past two when the *Lawrence* dropped astern. I remember it quite well, although I was wounded. I believed she was about to strike, and I wanted the exact time for my log and the official report."

With his bandaged arm, he fumbled clumsily in a packet of papers he had brought ashore. Quietly his surgeon opened the packet and extracted the contents.

"Here it is, sir. I say here that it was half past two when you dropped astern. Then your small boat passed from the *Lawrence* to the *Niagara*, *which vessel at this time was perfectly fresh*."

He looked curiously at Perry. In a way, Perry realized, he should not discuss naval matters with an enemy officer, but he liked and trusted the gallant Englishman. In confidence, he told him of Elliott's charges.

The Englishman pulled himself to a sitting position, wincing at the pain.

"That chap, sir!" His voice was incredulous. "By jove, sir, he has his gall! If he had been one of our captains, we would have hoisted him on a whip rove through a yardarm!"

"Now, captain," his surgeon intervened smoothingly. He glanced at Perry, nodding toward the door. "You must not excite yourself, sir." As Perry quietly left, Barclay was still exclaiming over Elliott's behavior.

It was a boisterous evening. The villagers were in a rollicking mood and quite prepared to celebrate all night. Somehow, though he tried not to show it, Perry felt glum. The fever was bothering him again. And, he had to confess to himself, he was worried over the arbitrators' decision.

Vainly Harrison sought to shake him out of the depression. Perry sighed in frank relief when the torchlight parading ended shortly after midnight and the paraders, hoarse from cheering and shouldersore from holding aloft the big transparencies, began slipping off to their homes.

"I have a message from Elliott," Harrison said as he and Perry wearily climbed the stairs at the Hotel Duncan to their rooms.

"His choice is Lieutenant J. J. Edwards of the *Niagara*. He and Lieutenant Turner will meet early tomorrow morning—rather this morning—to study your report."

Perry nodded in satisfaction. "The sooner this controversy is settled, the better I'll like it."

Edwards was one of the officers Elliott had brought down with him from Sackett's Harbor. Though Perry did not know the lieutenant well, from what he had seen of him in action on the *Niagara*, he was convinced he was a good man. And Turner, the other arbitrator, he trusted implicitly. Though only nineteen years old, he had handled the brig *Caledonia* so smartly during the battle that Congress was awarding him a silver medal.

Trust those fellows to give an honest rendering, he thought drowsily, and then fell into a heavy sleep. Perry, in fact, slept so soundly that Harrison had to shake him awake in the morning, clucking that he hugged his bed like a new recruit.

"The arbitrators' report?" Perry asked quickly.

Harrison shook his head. "Not yet. Perhaps half an hour. But I wanted to give you time to dress while I wait on them."

Young Jimmy had already left their room, and Perry waited out the ordeal alone. Surely I trust Turner and Edwards, he thought, but honest men can have honest differences of opinion. Why are they taking so long? It's all there in simple black and white, and unless they are finding some defense for Elliott, they should have long since finished.

The possibility that they were drafting an alteration made him sweat. He had given his word, of course, and he would have to stand by it. But, God, the pure hell that would erupt through the Lake Erie command! He reproached himself for having given Elliott this added chance for making trouble.

Without knocking, Harrison burst into the room, and the expression on his face betrayed the verdict.

"Both arbitrators freely express the opinion that the report, as you originally wrote it, is correct, sir!" The general's heavy voice boomed triumphantly. "Congratulations, Commodore!"

To hide the relief on his face, Perry turned quickly toward the window. He stared across Erie Harbor to where the *Niagara* was riding restlessly at anchor.

"I will send Captain Elliott a letter advising him of the decision," he said quietly. "It should not surprise him, but it will be a blow, none the less."

He turned to face Harrison. "It has been a strain, General," he admitted simply. "But this should end it. When I turn over the command to Elliott, it will all be ended. In time, I trust, for his sake as for the Navy's, it will be forgotten."

Harrison was never a man to conceal his emotions easily, and now his uneasiness showed plainly.

"I am not so sure, Ollie." He hesitated momentarily. "I deplore saying this, but Captain Elliott is not the man his father was. Not by a damn sight, sir! I very much fear that you have not heard the last of Captain Jesse D. Elliott. I implore you to move carefully whenever your paths cross."

For a moment, so wild was the look on Elliott's face that the prudent Commodore Chauncey thought of calling for his marine guard.

"Ruined because I followed your advice and 'edged away,'" Elliott almost shouted. "I see it now! You would have won much credit if I'd won. You suffer only mild discomfort that it's Perry instead. Either way, you were safe."

There was a hurt expression on Chauncey's face.

"Come, Lieutenant, you are unstrung."

"Sir, I request that you overrule the arbitrators' findings."

Honest surprise flashed across Chauncey's usually expressionless face. "That's obviously impossible, Mr. Elliott, though I hasten to add that I sympathize deeply."

"Then you won't support me?"

"'Support,' sir, is a curious word susceptible to many interpretations. In your present emotional state, you are being guided by wounded pride and envy. I 'support' a position, not an unstable personality."

"Sir!"

"I am sorry to speak so frankly, Elliott, though perhaps if I had lost out as badly, I too might feel as you do. Yes, I think I would find it quite impossible to forgive."

Chauncey smiled at the agitated lieutenant. "Let us put it this way, sir. You pursue whatever course you may choose, independently. I will continue to 'support' the same basic position I have always supported. I trust in the future, Mr. Elliott. I trust in the future."

CHAPTER 15

AT FIRST, though it was his own home on Washington Square, Oliver Perry felt himself a stranger in the house. It was easier resuming command of the Newport squadron where regulations guided a man than adjusting to undisciplined life: the fretting baby who had been born while he was at Erie . . . the absence of fierce-eyed old Grandfather Perry who had died during the same period.

It was Elizabeth, loving, faithful, still-beautiful Elna, who eased him patiently over the transition.

Gradually Perry felt himself relaxing into a comfortable domesticity, but in his self-reproachful way, he chided himself for it. The news he heard was not good.

He had not been long home when Fort Niagara fell to General Drummond and his Indian allies. At the end of the year a similar fate overtook Buffalo and Black Rock. Perry tried to forget by immersing himself in Navy bureaucracy and finally arranging the more than deserved promotions for his officers at the beginning of the new year.

Still, he could not shut out the world, and he was alarmed that so many citizens gullibly swallowed the British peace feelers. Elna tried to divert his mind but, night after night, he could talk of little else. Having finished with Napoleon, the enemy could bring all her power to bear against the United States, he argued, and why would they want peace?

Quickly events justified his suspicions. Fort Oswego in New York fell in the spring, and before June, the British had intensified their blockade all along the New England coast. Perry swore in frustration.

Any fool could see it! Obviously, the British were determined to desolate the coast, ravage the seaport towns, destroy dockyards and terrorize the inhabitants. On the frontier they would do worse, letting their savages run wild. Yet Tory strength was rising daily, along with defeatist opposition to further prosecution of the war!

Finally, late in July, Perry was ordered to Baltimore to take command of the frigate *Java* and ready her for sea. Congress had authorized two flying squadrons to launch counterblows against the tight British blockade and retaliate for the sacking of seaboard towns. The *Java* assignment, he decided, was a bone from Washington in answer to his vain pleas to head up one of the squadrons.

Almost before he was settled on his new ship, the British struck simultaneously in two ways. While the peace meeting was getting underway at Ghent, they hit Fort Erie. They were repulsed, but immediately struck a heavier blow, entering Washington to burn, loot and rape.

With two old sea comrades, Commodore Rodgers and Captain Porter, Perry moved on the smoking capital, hoping to prevent the enemy from making a quiet and unavenged withdrawal down the Potomac. A few miles below Mount Vernon, Perry positioned his small force of seamen and marines at Indian Head and waited.

But the invaders were too strong. They overran the militia at Alexandria, withstood several sharp assaults by the forces of Rodgers and Porter and on September 6, laden down with the large quantities of plunder, descended on Indian Head.

In a way, Perry thought grimly, it was the story of British longs all over again. Except for one eighteen-pounder, his battery consisted of six-pounders, and the British long guns drove him to cover before he could maul their vessels. His meager supply of powder and shot expended, he swore in frustration as the British fleet disappeared downriver.

With Commodore Rodgers, he hastened back to Baltimore, which was now threatened with attack.

Grimly the citizens were filling powder horns, and Fort McHenry, which guarded the harbor, had its big guns ready. The two commanders mustered all available seamen to man the ramparts, and though he knew it would be a forlorn hope, Perry prepared the *Java* for a dash to sea if the British overran the town. Better go down fighting than strike, he decided.

From Philadelphia, which was similarly threatened, came word that hardened Baltimore's resolve. There, eighty-year-old Thomas McKean, one of the last surviving signers of the Declaration of Independence, had been brought down to the State House Square to stiffen weak spines. The only member of the Continental Congress who had served from its opening through to the peace, the old man might have resorted to Revolutionary slogans and memories, but he spoke with a harsh immediacy that stirred the beleaguered East.

"This is not a time for speaking but a time for acting. . . ." the frail voice said, and yet the words carried south to Baltimore, north to New York. "We have now nothing to do with the past, we must only think of the present and the future. . . . *There are now but two parties—our country and its invaders.*"

Baltimore settled down to await the attack.

Just a day short of a year since the British rout on Lake Erie, aboard H.M.S. *Gladiator*, moored in Portsmouth Harbor, Barclay's board of court-martial sat in awesome dignity. Presiding officer was Edward James Foote, rear admiral of the white and second officer in command at Spithead and Portsmouth, and seated with him were a dozen other senior officers.

First, in deference to the law passed in the reign of George II, entitled "An Act for amending, explaining and reducing into one Act of Parliament the Laws relating to the Government of His Majesty's Ships, Vessels and Forces at Sea," the thirteen judges took several prescribed oaths that they would do their duty.

Then the defendant was led in and at the sight of the withered man who had been wounded eight times in sixteen years of fighting for the Crown, the women spectators cried.

Quietly Barclay submitted a written defense and then hobbled to the stand. "Have you any complaint to make against any of the officers or crews of the squadron under your command in Lake Erie?" he was asked.

"None."

A similar question, whether they had any complaint against Barclay, was asked of the officers. "None whatever."

It was Barclay's intention to show that he had fought out of necessity, not rashness, and had been beaten because he was undermanned and underprovisioned. Through his witnesses he maintained that the *Lawrence* alone had carried more able seamen than all his squadron and that the matches and tubes supplied him at Amherstburg had been so defective that his men had to fire pistols at the guns all through the engagement to set them off.

One after another his surviving officers corroborated his own description of his plight, and though Barclay himself refrained from discussing the *Niagara's* curious maneuvering, many of the other witnesses mentioned it. Thus, the British court-martial reached a peculiar climax —unreserved acquittal for Barclay and his men who had "conducted themselves in the most gallant Manner" and a tacit condemnation of United States Captain Jesse Elliott, three thousand miles away.

On the morning of September 11, a year and a day after the Erie battle, the British landed 5,000 mercenaries and 4,000 marines at the mouth of the Patapsco River. They hit General Strickler's brigade, along with some Pennsylvania volunteers, and tried to turn the American flank. Coolly the Americans retired in good order to their previously prepared fortifications and made plans for a counterattack the following day.

Instead, the enemy decamped overnight, returned to their ships, and the next day attacked Fort McHenry by water. *There are now but two parties—our country and its invaders.* From McHenry erupted such a rain of metal that the battered British ships fled under cover of darkness. Withdrawing to the safe mouth of Chesapeake Bay, they clamped down a tightened blockade.

Baltimore had been saved, and Perry's *Java*, rigged, provisioned, ready for sea, had been spared. But she was useless. Though fully manned, she could scarcely beard the entire British fleet that lay outside.

The *Java* lay idly at her moorings as crewmen holystoned her decks to gleaming whiteness, ran through station drills and practiced gunnery, while Perry despaired at home. The glowing coals in the fireplace gave out a cheery warmth, and Perry stretched luxuriously in his easy chair. His boots were lying beside the footstool, and he wriggled his toes within the heavy stockings, feeling the familiar tug between comfort and the call of duty.

Why should he be here in front of a pleasant fire while other captains were pacing ice-studded quarter-decks? Why did he have to serve as housekeeper to a checkmated ship while Andy Jackson's men were getting ready to fight in New Orleans? With a pang of envy that he hated to admit, he thought of his good friend, Steve Decatur. Months ago he had heard that Steve was getting the *President*, a big forty-four gunner, and now there were rumors that Steve was going to lead one of the flying squadrons against British shipping.

Perry slapped a weathered fist into his open palm, swearing softly. That was the assignment he had wanted. What a team he and Steve would have made, working their squadrons in close co-ordination!

So softly that he didn't hear her, Elizabeth came up behind his chair. "Still eating your heart out?" she said sadly. "You know, Father insists that you need a long rest from the sea, Ollie. He says the fever eats at you and will destroy you one day if you don't purge yourself of it."

"Dr. Mason is a very wise doctor, but he worries about everyone but himself. He sees phantoms in the rigging, Elna."

"But you *were* exhausted when you came home from Erie. Why, you were so weak. . . . Sometimes, I think you think of nothing but your country."

"Perhaps, my dear, but these are the critical years. The French, the British, even the Algerians think we are an easy mark. If we don't stand up and fight now, we'll lose all we gained only thirty-eight years ago."

The insistent jingling of the doorbell suddenly sounded. Perry turned to stare crossly at the bell which rocked slightly on its flexible housing.

"Who is calling at this time of evening!"

The bell pealed again. Reluctantly Perry rose, strolled toward the door and unlatched it. A gust of wind blew in, scattering ashes out of the fireplace. Then Elizabeth smiled as she heard her husband roar out a delighted welcome to their late visitor.

CHAPTER 16

"STEVE! Steve Decatur! What in the world are you doing here?"

"Freezing, by God, Ollie! Freezing! I'd take most kindly to a bit of time by the fire and a pot of grog or buttered rum. Don't you answer your bell, sir?"

Laughing at the sound of the familiar, booming voice, Elizabeth quickly came forward. "Steve!" she exclaimed. "How nice to see you again!"

Decatur swept off his large hat, took Elizabeth's outstretched hand, kissed it and bowed gallantly.

"By jove, madam, ye look warm and wonderful as ever!"

Elizabeth blushed, and her husband growled good-naturedly, "Still the damned continental dandy."

"Ignore him, madam. He spends too much time on the lakes with backwoodsmen."

Elizabeth laughed. "Do give me your coat and hat, and then I'll fetch some brandy."

As Elizabeth left them, Perry eagerly demanded to know the gossip going around in Washington, Decatur's plans, and whether he carried any new orders for him. But Decatur was in a teasing mood. Warming his backside against the fire, he studied Perry with mock respect.

"By God, sir! A damned bemedaled commodore in epaulets. Barclay's nemesis! Erie's hero! Come, show me your medals, Ollie. I'll bet you look like a French king with all that gold on your chest."

Perry, long accustomed to Decatur's boisterousness, promptly counterattacked.

"You've not smelled much gunsmoke lately, I hear. Hanging around New York like a jack tar at the main brace!"

"Aye," Decatur admitted wryly. "They pick Decatur to defend the big town, and so the British promptly go to Washington for easy pickings."

"They're afraid of you, Steve. But something tells me you're coming back now from Washington with a new command."

"I knew you'd heard. You met Porter while you were at Indian Head, admiring the scenery."

Perry winced. "It was little more," he conceded.

Elizabeth returned with the bandy, and there was silence as the commodore lifted his glass to her, then drank. "Ah!" He exhaled. "This is excellent, my dear madam."

Then, his splinter-scarred face suddenly serious, he explained his mission to Perry. He was bringing Perry orders to command one of the new flying squadrons. But Perry would first have to build the ships. After that, he would take them to the English coast and harass British shipping in its home waters.

"Good!" Perry growled. "I'll finally be seeing some action."

The orders specified that Perry supervise the construction of fast brigs at Warren and Middletown. The sites had been chosen because there were good timber stands available and little danger of British intervention. Perry also would retain command of the *Java*.

"That means little enough," Perry complained. "The whole damned British fleet blocks her passage."

"A compliment, Ollie. Look on it that way. They have a high opinion of you."

"And what did you draw?" Perry asked, suddenly suspicious. "Your high spirits are not entirely inspired by my good fortune."

"Warmer latitudes." Decatur chuckled. "A cruise to the lovely, romantic East Indies. They want a chap to break up British shipping there, too."

"I might have known," Perry grumbled. "You lucky dog. I always draw rough weather."

Elizabeth returned with more brandy. Decatur held his glass high, looking at Perry.

"Good hunting, mate!"

"That . . . that means Oliver is off again?" Elizabeth asked anxiously.

"Aye, madam. This time to England to splinter their coast trade as they've been doing to us."

"So far?" Her voice trailed off.

" 'Tis a choice assignment," Perry said consolingly. "And little danger, my dear, with fast brigs. They'll be fast, I warrant, for I'm to see them built."

"The sea!" she said bitterly. "Oh, I don't mean to complain, but . . . so far away . . ."

"Come, madam," Decatur boomed. "No tears from a commodore's wife. Come now, fetch me a little more brandy."

Decatur waited until Elizabeth had left the room. Then, dropping his voice, he said, "There are matters I'd prefer not to discuss in front of her, Ollie."

First off, he thought Perry should know that Elliott was still complaining, not only in New York but also in Washington, that he had not received justice.

"That's a dead cat," Perry said disgustedly. "He'll not get far."

"I don't know," Decatur warned. "Some of the officers are beginning to side with him. And then Barclay's court-martial puts the fat in the fire."

"The poor devil court-martialed! What did they do to him?"

"Exonerated Barclay but convicted Elliott."

"What are you saying?"

Decatur explained that the British inquiry had established that Elliott was making away with the *Niagara* when Perry went back to get her. While Barclay had remained silent on the subject, some of his officers had expressed themselves vigorously about Captain Elliott's conduct.

Sooner or later, Decatur speculated, some enterprising American journalist would get wind of the story. Then Elliott, in self-defense, would either call Perry out or demand a court of inquiry. That is, if he could stand an investigation.

"I'm afraid he can," Perry said slowly. "My report doesn't bear out any imputation of cowardice. In fact, I used the word 'gallantly' in referring to his action."

Decatur whistled in amazement. "So that's why there's been no inquiry already! What made you do it, Ollie?"

"You're one of the few men who could understand. You love this

Navy the way I do. You don't want any scandal at a time when we need every officer, every man, every ship we can muster, do you? I knew public exposure of Elliott's conduct would only hurt the Navy and not possibly help it in any way." He shrugged resignedly.

"Aye, I understand," Decatur said. "Probably would have done the same fool thing myself. And it was foolish, Ollie, no sense hiding that now."

Elizabeth returned with his glass, and Decatur quickly changed the topic of conversation.

"Frantic place, Washington," he growled. "Glad to get away from it. Madison is nervous as an apprentice in the maintop. The Secretary is screaming for more ships and guns. Congress, naturally, is filled with indignant speeches. Landsmen, bah!"

"There's been winds from poor quarters this year," Perry agreed.

Decatur nodded gloomily, applying himself to the brandy. Finally, putting down the empty glass, he rose. "If you will fetch my hat and coat, Ollie, I'd best be off."

"Steve, you just got here!"

"Not even staying overnight!" Elizabeth exclaimed in disappointment.

"My deepest regrets, madam. But I must leave."

As Perry helped his friend into his coat, he observed dryly, "Now that you have read and interpreted my orders, might I have them, just for the record?"

"By God, I completely forgot!" Decatur looked through his coat pockets and finally found the packet. He turned for a moment on the doorsill. "Guard your binnacle, Ollie. Good night, my dear Elizabeth."

Soberly Perry walked to the fireplace, unsealed the orders, and read them slowly. His brow furrowed in thought.

"Why so grave?" Elizabeth asked.

"Studying my new assignment as a commodore should." But he was thinking, more and more I fear my mistake at Erie will come home to my quarter-deck some day.

With the same unsparing drive that had brought his Lake Erie squadron into being, Perry directed the speedy construction of the brigs, *Chippewa*, *Saranac* and *Boxer*, at Middletown and Warren. He had little time for home, for he also was commanding the Newport Station and the immobilized *Java*.

Despite the peace negotiations at Ghent, the winds still blew ill for the United States, and Perry was especially grieved to hear of Steve Decatur's misfortunes.

Taking the big *President* out of New York harbor in a gale, Decatur grounded the forty-four gunner, and she came off "hogged"—twisted and warped from the grinding. Her rudder braces were snapped, a large part of the false keel carried away, and she failed to answer her helm smartly.

Then, as he was working her home for repairs, Decatur ran into a covey of British frigates. He drove the *Endymion* out of the action and, under a full press of sail, from the royal studding sails down, tried to shake loose from the other three.

But the *President* was a dull sailer, and Decatur found himself surrounded by the *Pomone* and the *Tenedos*, each thirty-eight gunners, and the big razee, *Majestic*, with fifty-six guns. Almost a hundred of his men dead or wounded—one-fourth the crew—Decatur had to strike as the razee prepared to tack and rake.

By the time Perry's three brigs were rigged and ready, Congress had ratified the Treaty of Ghent. He was delighted over the peace, but he couldn't shake off the letdown of a fighting man, and he turned his energies to the *Java*, taking her to sea for the first time. He was shocked that American contractors would build such a ship for their own Navy in wartime.

Through their inexclusable neglect or dishonesty, many of the *Java's* spars and much of her rigging proved weak and imperfect. She did not answer her helm quickly, her gun mountings seemed suspiciously fragile to his practiced eye and she had a nasty tendency to a starboard list.

Nothing but extensive overhaul would redeem her, Perry decided, and he took the sluggish frigate to Newport. At least, he had been able to gather round him the cream of his *Lawrence* veterans, he thought in self-consolation. Yarnall, Forrest, Hambleton, Doc Parsons, faithful Hannibal and the other three seamen who had rowed him to the *Niagara*.

Then the unexpected happened.

Paroled by the British, Steve Decatur came home, a subdued and embarrassed man, to receive a hero's welcome from the public and the government—and the inevitable court of inquiry from his own service.

"God, how I hated to strike!" he exclaimed to Perry when they met. All his booming high spirits had vanished, and the anguish was plain on his scarred face.

"It was the only thing, Steve. They were shooting you to splinters."

"Aye, but it doesn't lessen the hurt. A hundred dead or wounded, three lieutenants gone, and poor old Reuben James. You remember him, Ollie?"

Perry did. Long before, at Tripoli, the tar had taken a wicked cutlass slash aimed at Decatur. "They shot him to doll rags, Ollie!" There was a catch in the big man's voice.

Anyhow, Perry reminded him, the action had followed the signing of the Treaty of Ghent, and, by striking, Decatur had averted further loss of life in a postwar battle. Decatur nodded numbly.

But even the honorable acquittal, without reservation, that shortly followed did not seem to lift Decatur's spirits, and Perry worried more and more over him. Then, suddenly, there was a development that drove even his closest friend from his mind.

The accounts of Barclay's court-martial at Portsmouth had finally reached the American press, and Elliott reacted promptly. In answer to the British charges that he had been running away when he should have been carrying the fight to the *Queen Charlotte*, he demanded an inquiry by same board that had sat in New York to hear Decatur.

Irony, and more, Perry thought bitterly, that the court convened for his friend should become Elliott's instrument to remove the cloud on his reputation and, by inference, place one on Perry's name. Then Yarnall and Forrest were summoned to testify at the inquiry. Since the New York yards had the best facilities in the country, Perry decided to take the *Java* there. He could be close to the inquiry, though he had no intention of appearing there.

During the three days of Elliott's inquiry late in April, Perry stayed away from the courtroom, as he had promised himself. But he did not like what he heard each day from his officers who were attending.

Navy Secretary Benjamin Williams Crowninshield, a civilian appointed to the job only four months previously by President Madison, was personally attending the sessions. That seemed a bit odd, and to cap it, so was Commodore Chauncey, Elliott's long-time protector. By now, Perry suspected, crafty old Chauncey had the elegant, British-educated Mr. Crowninshield wrapped around his stubby fingers.

Perry, however, had faith in the president of the court, salty old Alexander Murray. Like Perry's own father, Murray's fighting days reached back to the Revolutionary Navy. He had seen action, been wounded and captured in thirteen land and sea engagements.

Alex Murray was not the kind of naval officer to look kindly on a man who ran away, but there were two others on the court, Evans and Rogers, to be reckoned with. Both were friends of Elliott, and protégés of Chauncey.

Finally, there was the judge advocate, an unknown factor, for Henry Wheaton was a civilian lawyer and diplomat. True, he had formerly been a division judge advocate in the Army; but how, Perry wondered, did that qualify him to sit as a newly appointed Justice of the Marine Court and naval prosecutor? Was it only coincidental that he also was a close friend of Elliott and the disgraced Barron?

The more Perry thought about it, the more he realized that Sam Hambleton, Steve Decatur and all the rest of his friends had been right. There *was* a conspiracy afoot that seemed to have two prongs: the rehabilitation and service preferment of Mr. Elliott and men like him and the sly downgrading of Decatur, himself and other fighting leaders of the Navy.

The chair commodores, the dockyard heros versus the men of the quarter-decks, he thought scornfully. These were the ugly little plottings of men who could capture promotion only by stealth and not by a fair fight at sea. But, in their own way, good fighters, he conceded ruefully. Already, Elliott had won the opening round with a stacked board.

CHAPTER 17

THOUGH he prided himself that the yoke of discipline had tamed his impatient spirit, Oliver Perry had to admit that hearing the inquiry's progress second-hand was getting on his nerves. He stood alone at the taffrail of the *Java* in New York harbor, nervously drumming his fingers as he waited for Forrest to return from the day's session.

Elliott had been clever in twisting Barclay's court-martial to his own advantage. He made himself out to be an innocent, brave young American officer whose reputation was being wantonly maligned by the British, only a few months ago the enemy and still roundly hated.

The technique reminded Perry of a talk with one of Harrison's lawyer-aides one night during the Thames River campaign. In law, he had explained to Perry, if you don't have a good defense, attack the law, attack the prosecutor—always attack, attack, attack! In the confusion, you can often get an acquittal for your client.

Now Elliott was attacking the British and, by implication, Perry himself. If he already had Evans and Rogers on his side, the stratagem should easily confuse a couple of civilians like Wheaton and Crowninshield.

When the small boat bumped gently alongside the *Java*, Perry had to restrain himself from hastening to Forrest.

"Captain Perry? Is that you, sir?"

"Aye." He managed to keep his voice calm. He turned, shielding his eyes in the dim light cast by the battle lanterns through their horn shells.

"And how did it go today, Mr. Forrest?"

The young officer did not answer immediately. "I wish you had been there to challenge certain testimony, sir," he said finally.

"Indeed, sir? They dare not summon me, and I would not testify voluntarily. Who were the day's chief witnesses?"

Tatem, the ruddy-faced master's mate of the *Niagara*, and Webster, her sailing master, Forrest told him.

"Good seamen both. Good seamen. I'll warrant their words made an impression."

"Aye," Forrest said reluctantly. "Tatem testified that the *Niagara's* helm was up and she was bearing down on the British when you boarded her."

"What! A landsman couldn't have mistaken her direction. And Webster? Did he support this lie?"

"Dodged the issue, sir. Said he was below and couldn't say whether the *Niagara's* helm was up or not."

Indignantly Forrest expressed his opinion of the board for not getting a proper answer from Webster.

"Did you ever hear such bilge, sir! A veteran tar can't tell what's goin' on in the rigging when he's below decks? She lifts like a gull when the helm's up and you can hear the water brushing her sides and feel the lee rail drop. Yet not a question thrown at him!"

"Aye," Perry said thoughtfully. "He would have known. I found him an excellent sailing master."

"Then was he on deck when you boarded the *Niagara*, sir?"

Perry was taken aback as he caught the full implication of Forrest's question.

"Let me think a moment, Mr. Forrest. This is most important. Aye, aye, he was on deck when I boarded. Now I remember distinctly. I gave him the order to back the maintop so we wouldn't run entirely out of the action. Then I told him to brail up the trysail and put the helm up to run down before the wind."

"I knew the rascal was dodging!" Forrest exclaimed triumphantly. Then his voice dropped in discouragement. "But what of it, sir? His testimony is in the record, and unchallenged. And I fear they wouldn't call you now, even if you were to attend the hearing."

Perry tugged nervously at one sideburn. "Aye, they've gone further than I dreamed they would dare."

The next night, it was Yarnall who briefed him, far more bluntly and profanely than the younger, respectful Forrest.

"Goddammit, sir, they've rigged this thing against you shamefully! Take every one of Elliott's witnesses—Webster, Tatem, Montgomery, Cummings, Adams. I don't need a sounding lead to understand them. Every lying bastard is up for promotion and under Chauncey's jurisdiction!"

Perry nodded wearily.

"And yet, sir, you still say Forrest and I can't let go with full broadsides at this hearing?"

"I still say it, Mr. Yarnall," Perry said quietly. "It would not be proper for me to interfere in any way with such an inquiry."

Yarnall shook his head in exasperation. "I'll do my best, sir," he grumbled, "but damned if I know why. Good night, sir."

"Good night, Mr. Yarnall."

Between the hate that burned insatiably, the coaching of the dull, frightened witnesses—and the feeling that all along he had somehow been just a cat's-paw of the wily Chauncey—Lieutenant Elliott had become a remarkably short-tempered man.

Now, though he knew he needed the services of the creature sitting with him in the gloomy little grog shop, he could not conceal his distaste.

"I must say, Heath, that neither your manners nor appearance have improved since we last met."

Marine Captain John Heath hiccuped gently and wiped the sweat from his forehead with his sleeve.

"I didn't come here at your bidding, sir, to be insulted," he said, almost whiningly. "I does the best I can."

Elliott's tone softened. "Of course you do. And because I'm your friend, Heath, I am going to make a suggestion about your next sea assignment."

Wariness showed briefly on Heath's pudgy face.

"I have important friends in the Navy, Heath, and I can do more than suggest—I can arrange your assignment to the Java."

"Serve under that damned self-righteous prig of a Perry, sir! You know my little weaknesses, sir."

"I know all about them, and in the past I've been very considerate in overlooking them. In the past, Heath. As I said, I have very important friends in the Navy, and your little weaknesses, as you call them, may not be overlooked in the future."

With the bravado of a weak man, Heath tried to stand on his dignity. "I don't think I have to take threats, sir."

Elliott's eyes suddenly blazed. "Come off it!" he said roughly. "I hate that blasted, pious martinet of a Perry more than you can possibly guess. What do you think the Navy will be like if his kind get the upper hand? Where do you think you will end up? I'll tell you! From your dirty uniform to your dirty girls to your drinking to your insolence, you won't last ten minutes. If they could do what they did to Jim Barron, what chance would you have under the Perrys and Decaturs?"

Elliott's wild outburst rattled Heath. He gulped a drink to steady himself, then asked, wheedlingly, "But why, sir, should I then serve directly under him? Putting my head in the lion's mouth, you might say."

"Because you're—you," Elliott retorted. "Because the very sight of you will get on his nerves till he loses his temper and does something rash. Trust Mr. Perry to be rash! He may even strike you."

"I wouldn't like that, sir." The liquor had steadied Heath. "I would prefer charges against him."

"Exactly. And that is the way we will break Mr. Perry. And then, if we can, Mr. Decatur, and the other high-and-mighty sea cocks."

His voice dropped persuasively. "Heath, my important friends are going to control the Navy. If you do what I say, they will remember *you favorably. If you don't, they will remember, too. And the other side wouldn't accept you under any circumstances."*

"Looks like I have no choice," Heath muttered.

"You really don't, Heath," Elliott said. "You really don't! Now sit a little closer while I give you your sailing orders."

April 26th, 1815

In the gathering darkness, Perry stood alone on the *Java* as lights began to flicker in the houses ashore and the city's squat skyline merged with the low clouds. Five bells. Topmen now were igniting the riding lights of other ships in the harbor, and his men would be back momentarily from the Elliott inquiry.

He removed his elbows from the taffrail and paced back and forth, hands clenched behind him.

The farce, to which he had so naïvely contributed, must be ended. And, Perry thought, he knew Mr. Elliott's curtain lines: page two, line twelve of Perry's own report. "At half past two, the wind springing up, Captain Elliott was enabled to bring his vessel, the *Niagara*, gallantly into close action."

Ha! She'd been a full half-mile off the *Lawrence's* weather bow when that brave hulk had been within a good pistol shot of both the *Detroit* and the *Queen Charlotte*. No matter. He had acted for the good of the service, as he saw it, and he could not now undo the past.

Absorbed in thought, he failed to hear the boatswain's pipe sounding the arrival of a ranking officer aboard. "Ollie!" The familiar voice startled him.

"Steve Decatur! You've brought Forrest back safely. Where's Yarnall?'

"Looking after some equipment they're stowing forward for work tomorrow, sir," Forrest said. He sounded distressed. "I waited for Commodore Decatur, sir. Thought you might prefer to hear the results from him."

"I daresay I can do a good job of guessing," Perry said grimly.

Decatur avoided Perry's eyes, moving restlessly to the taffrail to stare out across the harbor.

"It's a pleasure to be with seamen, sir, after watching rabbits for three days. Quite a showman, Elliott."

124

"They let him off, of course?"

"Aye. I think if I were ten years younger, I might call the rascal out, but you never win a duel."

Forrest coughed. "I tried to stick to your report, sir, but my conscience compelled me to testify that there should have been more sail set on the *Niagara*."

Decatur laughed humorlessly. "They sure as hell looked startled when Yarnall estimated the *Niagara* was at least three-quarters of a mile away and could have been brought to closer action."

Even though Commodore Murray bore a good reputation, Decatur grumbled, he'd had little to say, letting Elliott's two friends on the board, Evans and Rogers, do all the questioning.

"That civilian, Wheaton, sure acted confused," Forrest interjected.

"Acted like he was doing everything on cue," Decatur corrected him. "Wrote the report, too, in his best diplomatic prose. The court regrets any diversity of opinion, blah, blah. The court feels, blah, blah, that attempts made to wrest away the laurels won by Captain Elliott should not lessen him in the opinion of his fellow citizens."

"The laurels *won* by Mr. Elliott? Perry asked dryly.

"Wheaton's word, Ollie. But hark to this! The court feels that, actually, the *Queen Charlotte* made away from the *Niagara*! God's truth! That's what they found."

Further, having sat in on the hearings, Secretary Crowninshield promptly approved the report.

"Crowninshield had no other choice," Perry said tiredly. "Elliott had put the honor of our Navy against the word of British officers. What would you have done?"

Decatur nodded reluctantly. "Aye, the honor of our Navy."

Seven bells sounded forward, and Decatur started. "Damn! I promised I'd be on time tonight. There's a ball being given for Bainbridge and me."

"Just because you and Bainbridge have got the choice Mediterranean squadrons," Perry teased. "With plush assignments like that, *you* should be giving the ball."

"All right, come along as my guest. Many of your friends will be there, and champagne may help you forget this Elliott business."

Good idea, Perry thought. Forrest had the next watch, and Yarnall was not going ashore, so the *Java* was in good hands.

"Accepted, Steve!" He turned to Forrest. "Some marines will be reporting aboard in the morning, mister. See that they are assigned hammock space and get their gear squared away. We have no commander of the guard as yet."

Silently Decatur accompanied Perry to his cabin so he could change into his dress uniform. Perry explained that he was a little annoyed at not having a marine commander. With the *Java*, he rated a captain and had asked for one, but there was a holdup.

"Washington assigned me a man, but apparently he won't resume active duty for another couple of months."

Strange, Decatur mused, that there were not other captains available and that Perry had to wait for a particular man. Perry shrugged his shoulders. "Just a custom of the service, Steve."

Again, Decatur fell silent, but as the cutter was taking them ashore, he brought up the subject again.

"The fellow asked for the *Java*," Perry said patiently. "And, after all, we're in no hurry. Half the spars and most of the rigging must be replaced."

"Know his name?"

"I'm told it's Heath. Captain John Heath."

"Well, I'll be damned!" Decatur glanced toward the rowers, and dropped his voice. "As soon as we're ashore, I want a private word with you."

As they swayed and bumped in a carriage en route to the hotel ballroom, Decatur spoke. It seemed an odd coincidence, he said, that a marine captain should specifically ask for the *Java* when other ships readying for departure to foreign stations were short on officers, too. It seemed even more coincidental, he went on, that Captain Heath happened to be a friend of Captain Elliott.

"A very good friend, I've known for some time," he emphasized.

"Don't spoil a pleasant evening with more suspicions about Elliott!" Perry exclaimed. "I want to forget him!"

"I'm blunt and I'm loud, Ollie, but I have almost a woman's feelings about such things. Watch this Captain Heath!"

Perry could not help laughing.

"Oh, Steve! You do sound like a woman! What can a lone captain of marines do to a ship's captain?"

Decatur refused to be amused. "If he's a trouble maker, he can do a lot in his position. He can start false rumors, play a Judas sheep, raise Old Ned with the discipline."

"Remember, Steve, I expect to have some say aboard the *Java*."

"All right, Ollie. I've warned you. One thing more, and I promise

I'll say no more on the subject all evening. If I were you—and I don't think I'm exactly a timid man—I'd be most careful if ever I came under Chauncey's command again!"

CHAPTER 18

IN ALL, there were four Barbary kingdoms—Algiers, Morocco, Tripoli and Tunis—whose chief industries were the export of pirates and the import of slaves and booty. As fiefs of the Turkish Empire they were ruled by the Sultan's janissaries, but their dedication to sea brigandry was historically notorious. Since they were chiefly Moorish, with some Arab and tribal minorities, they preyed especially on Christian ships, putting the men to the sword, or enslaving them, and kidnaping the women for their harems.

Whenever the civilized powers were distracted by their private quarrels, the Barbary corsairs ranged far over the Mediterranean. During the Napoleonic Wars, they haunted the coasts of the Italian states, hitting Sardinia and Naples hard. While the United States was fighting Britain, they grabbed an American merchantman, the *Edwin*, enslaving its crew of ten and one passenger. From all nations they demanded tribute.

With amused indulgence, Perry thought of his young little country. Barely out of one war with the biggest sea power in the world, the United States was now committed to a second against Algiers. Two Mediterranean squadrons, under Bainbridge and Decatur, were being readied to sail momentarily.

Though he lamented the unreadiness of the *Java* which meant that he would have to stay behind, Perry had to give Crowninshield, or someone in Washington, credit for assigning precisely the right commanders for the mission. Both Bainbridge and Decatur had old personal grudges to settle with the Barbary Coast.

Less than a dozen years earlier, grounded on a rock, surrounded by Tripolitan gunboats, Bainbridge had been forced to strike the forty-four-gun *Philadelphia*. Though Decatur managed to burn the captured vessel in the enemy port of Tripoli, Bainbridge languished for nineteen months in a dungeon of the Bashaw of Tripoli. And Decatur, who had emerged the hero of that war, carried a more burning hatred of the pirates. His younger brother had been killed by them.

Now Steve was supposed to convince the Dey of Algiers, once and for all, that his corsairs must expect no tribute, slaves or loot from American shipping. Since the Dey respected the British for having the most powerful fleet in the world, and *they* accepted his demands, Decatur had some real convincing to do.

But he planned a simple, forthright approach, he confided to Perry. Algiers had not been attacked since 1541 when Charles the Fifth ill-advisedly took his Spanish Armada into the harbor, and promptly met disaster. None the less, Decatur was going to make straight for Rais Hammida, admiral of the Algerian fleet.

"Ollie, I promise you, he'll strike or die."

There had been no bombast in the big man's voice and, Perry thought happily, Hammida and his turbaned sailors with their baggy trousers are going to get one great big shock! I'd bet a cask of Madeira against a pot of it that Steve beats Bainbridge to the first strike.

Now it was mid-May, and Decatur's squadron was anchored in New York harbor tauntingly close to the dock-bound *Java.*

Well out near Staten Island, Decatur's trim new flagship, the *Guerrière*, named for her predecessor, the English frigate taken by Commodore Hull in *Old Ironsides*, was riding gently in the outgoing tide. Nearby, he picked out the silhouette of the big *Macedonian*, the English prize which Steve had taken after completely dismasting her.

Slowly Perry ticked off the rest of Steve's smart, ready squadron: *Constellation, Ontario, Epervier, Fire-fly, Flambeau, Spark, Spitfire, Torch.* The *Ontario*—— She was only a sloop, but Perry frowned as he studied her. Captain Elliott had been given her command. He would be sailing with Decatur while Perry mothered his *Java.*

Though Decatur was standing out to sea on the morrow and Perry was again indulging his unhappiness, this time Perry heard the boatswain's pipe. He hurried forward to meet the ranking officer who was boarding. At first, in the dusk, he scarcely recognized the tall, handsome figure in elegantly laced coat and hat, cassimere pantaloons and long boots bordered at the top with gold lace.

"Steve!" he exclaimed. "You insufferable dandy!"

Decatur grinned sheepishly. "My going-away clothes, Ollie. Just arrived from the tailor's. Tried 'em on for the fitting and then thought, dammit, I'll give old Perry a laugh. Think Mr. Hammida will approve?"

Perry laughed and brought his friend down to the master cabin where they could drink in privacy. They had a few drinks, and Decatur fidgeted. "Coat's a bit tight," he explained.

"Out with it, Steve! There's something on your mind."

Decatur sighed. "You've got me plain scared to talk on the subject, Ollie. But I couldn't rest, leaving tomorrow, unless I made one more stab. Let me go about it chronologically, and you keep still till I'm through."

"All right," Perry said as he filled the glass again. "Here's your drink —and my silence, sir."

Decatur launched on a leisurely history of the newfangled steamboats. Perry listened but could not figure what Decatur was trying to tell him.

There had been Rumsey back thirty years ago, Decatur rambled. Fellow on the Potomac forced water in aft and got power by expelling it at the stern. And many others—John Fitch, Millar, Read and the crazy artist Fulton.

"But only thirty-two hours up the Hudson to Albany, Ollie. Did it in the *Clermont*. And he's done well, too, with his *Car of Neptune*, *Paragon*, *Vesuvius*, *Olive Branch* and four or five more."

"They'll never replace the sailers, sir," Perry said firmly. "Give me a fair wind, following, and I'll run from any mechanical monster made!"

Decatur arched an eyebrow. "And with head winds, mister? How would you plow through head winds without your tacking?"

No, crazy or not, Fulton had really come up with something, just in the past few months. A forty-four gunner, the *Demologus*, designed by him and built by Noah and Adam Brown for the Navy.

"Damnedest thing I've ever seen, Ollie. Weird-looking. No lines to her. But she makes five knots on calm waters. I tell you, sir, some day steam craft like the *Demologus* will make sailers obsolete overnight. With a growing nation, we are going to have a growing, massive Navy and a *changed* Navy, sir."

Perry got up impatiently. "You've talked yourself dry, Steve, making it sound, somehow, like a lecture. Ease your mind. If I have to sail steam, I'll learn to sail steam. All there's to it."

Again Decatur sighed heavily. "Not my point at all. I come back to this hard-to-put-your-finger-on conspiracy. There's the claque, no doubt of it—Chauncey, Elliott and all the rest—including your precious

Captain Heath, I'm sure. There's the goal—*their* control of this shiny big new Navy. And there's the obstacle—you, probably me, and the other strong sea captains who came out of this war with England. It all fits together."

"And your parting instructions, Commodore?"

"Keep your guard up! Now I'm off to find Hammida. He's a raping heathen bastard, but I'm sure I'll be able to see him before he tries to strike. You mayn't be so lucky among the Christians."

Considering there were the two ocean crossings, east and westbound, a sea battle, a long bit of diplomatic haggling with the wily Dey and a Mediterranean cruise, Steve Decatur accomplished his mission with amazing speed.

As he had promised Perry, he found the Algerian flagship *Meshouda*, and Rais Hammida was killed in the fight. Then his squadron captured another twenty-two-gun brig which had run aground off Cartagena, and having thus pointedly made his presence felt, he was able to get a respectful audience with the Dey.

Not only did Decatur get the release of the American captives, but he also obtained freedom for a number of Danish and Sicilian prisoners as well. As an alternative to losing his entire fleet and his capital to American gunnery, Decatur heavily suggested, the Dey might consider signing the treaty to waive further exaction of tribute.

William Shaler, United States consul for the Regency of Algiers, did not like Decatur's tactics. He considered the Hero of Tripoli overbearing, vain and, worst of all, an advocate of powder-smoke diplomacy. Decatur, who did not like Shaler, either, figuring he was too friendly with the British, ignored him. Reluctantly the Dey decided that it would be more sagacious to go along with the big man in the splendid Navy uniform. He signed the treaty.

Powder smoke or not, Decatur thus administered the death blow to a cruel, ancient custom which had harassed Christendom for centuries, and still he was not satisfied. He proceeded to Tunis, demanding, and getting, from the Bey, indemnity for treaty violations. At Tripoli, he was similarly successful with the frightened Pacha who remembered him all too well.

In a triumphal cruise of the principal Mediterranean ports, he was hailed as the savior of Europe who had forever broken the dark power of the Barbary states. That November, only six months after his squadron had weighed anchor in New York, he sailed home to a near hysterical hero's welcome. Even President Madison, in his message to Congress, began with sonorous praise of Decatur's achievements, though Perry put it in pithier, warmer fashion.

"You oversized continental dandy!" he growled. "You talk big and damned if you don't act big!"

Decatur's return meant action at last for Perry, and he blessed his friend's name. Steve had brought home a copy of the proposed treaty with the Dey of Algiers for ratification by Congress. It was approved early in January 1816, and the day after Forrest returned from Washington with the signed copy, the *Java* put to sea from Newport to deliver it.

Pacing his quarter-deck, hungrily inhaling the fresh salt air, Perry grinned to himself. For Steve Decatur, success had come with an ironic twist. Along with Rodgers and Porter, he had been appointed to the first three-man Board of Navy Commissioners, and he was building a handsome residence in Washington.

But now he was deskbound and he lamented in a letter to Perry, which Forrest had delivered along with the treaty: "After all, my dear friend, what shall I do? We have no war, nor signs of war, and I shall feel ashamed to die in my bed." Too bad, Perry thought unsympathetically. After all, it's my turn. He chuckled that the situation was now reversed, and he was at sea while Steve remained at home.

Along with the precious treaty, the *Java* carried one passenger, Tom Anderson, the likable, lively little fellow whom President Madison had nominated as consul for the Regency of Algiers. Perry did not understand the appointment. From what Decatur had told him, Shaler, who already held the Algerian post, intended to remain in service there.

"I think the President just made a mistake, everything's so topsy-turvy in Washington," Forrest ventured. "I have a hunch Madison had intended to nominate Anderson for some other consular post, but in his hurry to get the treaty ratified, he slipped. What do you think, sir?"

Perry shrugged noncommittally. He wondered frankly whether Decatur might have had a hand in the apparent move to replace Shaler, but, out of loyalty to his friend, he said nothing. Anyhow, it would be unlike Steve to let personalities influence him.

In view of the importance of their mission, the *Java* made sail despite a gale from the northwest. In fourteen days, from the time they left Nantucket Shoals, its unrelenting fury drove the frigate to within a hundred miles of Cape St. Vincent. One seaman was lost overboard,

131

and Perry had the sad duty of reading services over five others. A falling main-topmast, which carried down with it the main-topmast yard and mizzen-topgallant-mast, had caught and crushed the poor devils.

Then the gale shifted, coming at them from the west, which forced them to lie to for two days. When they finally raised Gibraltar, they were twenty days out. Despite Perry's earlier misgivings, the *Java* had withstood the pounding and, not requiring urgent repairs, he decided against stopping. After communicating with shore, he laid a course for Malaga. The following morning, to everyone's relief, they dropped anchor at the Spanish port.

The men were tired and edgy, which was understandable, but there was also a curious undertone of sullenness which Perry could not account for. More and more, the officers reported disciplinary troubles, and Forrest roundly recommended the whip.

Perry, who detested floggings as debasing, thought he had a better solution. Before going on to Port Mahon, rendezvous of the Mediterranean Squadron, he would let the tars saturate themselves with the warm wine and women of the country.

Except for one occasion, which he later regretted, Perry did not go ashore. He spent the long, sunny, lazy days seeing to the instruction of the midshipmen in navigation, Spanish, French and use of the sword. He also had somewhat advanced ideas that all officers must be as polished gentlemen as possible. Much to the amusement of the tars, he made the embarrassed youngsters practice ballroom dancing steps.

Just once, at the insistence of Joe Macpherson, his executive officer, and Dulaney Forrest, he toured Malaga. He had not particularly wanted to go ashore, but Doc Parsons raised such a fuss against it, clucking that he needed rest, that Perry perversely decided he *would* go.

In their day-long tour of what Forrest called "the local places of interest," they consumed entirely too much of the rich, red wine.

The deceptively mild grape fragrance of the wine concealed a kick like a capstan bar when the pawl fails to lock. As they returned to the *Java*, Perry could feel the fever coming on, and by the time he had climbed aboard, he was barely strong enough to walk unaided to his cabin.

For two days he was bedded, tormented constantly by the sweats and shivers and nightmares, in which Elliott and Heath seemed to be whispering together and laughing at him.

When Doc Parsons brought him out of it, weak but convalescing,

Perry shamefacedly remembered the nightmares and hoped that he hadn't raved aloud.

None the less, Captain Heath was a strange one, all right. Perry could say that with a clear head and, somewhat uneasily, he recalled Decatur's warnings.

A sloppy fellow at best, the marine captain seemed to try to accentuate his slovenliness. His hands were always stuffed in his pockets in inexcusably unmilitary fashion, and he walked with a forced, unnecessary swagger. Usually his clothes were unpressed and often even soiled.

What bothered Perry most was that Heath gave every indication of trying to bait him. His manner verged on the disrespectful, his pudgy face had a chronically petulant, disdainful cast, and he executed orders with irritating casualness.

Theoretically he and his men should have been examples of disciplined alacrity to the rest of the crew. But, time and again, Macpherson, Yarnall and Forrest complained to Perry that, like their commander, the Marine guard was definitely averse to following orders promptly.

Though he was still irritable from the fever, Perry refrained from dressing down Heath. He preferred to think that after the rough Atlantic passage the warm Mediterranean sun would improve the attitude of Heath and the men he influenced. If not, there was bound to be trouble aboard.

CHAPTER 19

FORTUNATELY the *Java* had an easy passage from Malaga to Port Mahon, capital and principal port of the Balearic Islands. During the run, Perry rested comfortably, trying to regain his strength. Occasionally, as an aftermath of the fever, his nerves would jangle unbearably, and then he would pace the quarter-deck as though he could walk the ailment out of his system.

Though he was not completely recovered, he had sufficiently studied theatrics to fool Doc Parsons. Despite Perry's faint stomach pains and feverish seizures during the night hours, the Doc was convinced of his recovery by the time the *Java* stood into the deep, narrow inlet on the southeast side of the island.

Somewhat shakily, Perry went ashore to attend to the stately naval courtesies due the other commanding officers of the squadron by a new arrival. Usually Perry rather enjoyed such amenities, but today he felt an impatience difficult to conceal. He was surprised at his own intense reaction when Commodore Bainbridge gave him the good news.

Smiling broadly, the veteran officer announced that orders for the *Java* to return to the States reportedly were coming on the *Washington*, a huge new seventy-four gunner. Bainbridge had no idea who her commander might be, but he obligingly promised Perry that he would make the necessary arrangements for the *Java* to fall in with the *Washington* at the first report of her whereabouts.

Perry found his hands trembling. Why, I'm consumed with a desire to get home, he realized. It had never happened before. Next to Elna, the sea was his life. He had always craved active duty, and no cruise had tired him before. He could not understand it. Bainbridge was looking at him curiously, and he flushed as he realized he had failed to answer a question.

Maybe, he argued to himself, going back to the *Java*, that rough passage to Gibraltar did it. Certainly knocked the tar out of all of us. No, might as well face up to it—there was a nagging little presentiment of impending trouble. Oh, if he could only weigh anchor now for Algeria, drop off Tom Anderson and the treaty, then set a course for Newport under a full press of canvas!

Back on the frigate, he took one look at the thunderclouds on Yarnall's face and knew there was trouble. "May I have a word with you, sir?" Yarnall said. Perry beckoned him to follow him to his cabin. This must be about discipline, and he didn't want any of the tars to overhear them.

"As I understand, sir, it was the captain's expressed desire here at Mahon that at least a third of the guard and seamen remain aboard."

"That is correct, Mr. Yarnall."

"This day, our arrival, has been disgraceful, sir! Seamen jumping overboard and swimming ashore without leave!" Yarnall was outraged but, worse from a career man's point of view, mortified that such conduct had been observed by the other vessels in port.

"Didn't the marines attempt to stop them?"

"Those bastards jumped in, too, and swam ashore with them."

If the matter hadn't been so serious, Perry would have had to laugh at Yarnall's shocked incredulity.

"And Mr. Heath?"

"Bah!" Perry had never seen his subordinate so angry since the day they had both watched Elliott making away from them in the *Niagara*. "I provided ready boats for pursuit, sir, but Mr. Heath seemed interested only in the feminine and alcoholic enticements ashore. He made no attempt whatsoever to stop them."

"Very good, Mr. Yarnall. I shall take the necessary steps."

"Thank you, sir. I—I suppose there is no point in again recommending floggings, sir?"

"No, Mr. Yarnall."

From Doc Parsons, Perry got blunt confirmation of Heath's conduct during the next few days. After the first wild outburst the men had settled down somewhat, but the marine captain absented himself almost constantly from the *Java*. Usually, when present, he reported himself "indisposed," but his only medicine seemed to be limitless supplies of wine which he smuggled aboard, Parsons reported dryly.

Since Macpherson was his executive officer, Perry preferred to pass word through him, rather than through the blunter Yarnall, that discipline was to be tightened. He also promulgated an order that all seamen *and* marines were to attend to the cleanliness of their uniforms. While he realized the marines' uniforms were frayed, and there were no new ones available at this station, they could at least be kept clean.

"I trust Mr. Heath will not consider me a martinet," he observed to Macpherson. "But we represent the United States, and it is of great importance that we make the best possible appearance."

"Tremendously important, sir, as I have tried to impress on Mr. Heath."

"The Spanish are filthy, and the corsairs are even worse," Perry said angrily. "But that's no valid reason why we should copy them! Clean them up, Mr. Macpherson, and keep them that way."

To Perry, with his strange hunger to get his mission done and get home again, the days at Mahon dragged maddeningly. Among the officers there was the smug feeling that the Barbary powers had now been humbled, and hence there was no need to hurry.

Then there was further, inevitable delay as command of the squadron passed from Bainbridge to Commodore John Shaw, an officer with a peculiar but impressive background. Born in Ireland, the son of a British officer, he had not come to the United States until he was seventeen. But, as Perry knew from his record, he had gallantly served his adopted country.

During an eight months' cruise in the little schooner *Enterprise* in hostilities with the French, he had fought five hot actions—two of them with superior forces—captured eight French privateers and recovered eleven American prizes. Yes, Shaw was Perry's hard-driving kind of Navy man, but of course he needed time to acquaint himself with his new command. It was April before the squadron finally left for Algiers.

Accompanied by Perry, Shaw visited the Dey for the seemingly routine procedure of exchanging the ratified treaty for one which Decatur had left with the Dey for his ratification. But the cunning Barbary chieftain had been having further thoughts, and he tried to put them off.

First, he charged that several articles in the original document had been altered. The Americans flushed at this calculated insult to the integrity of their country, but kept their tempers. Reading both copies word for word, Perry and Shaw pronounced them identical. Then the Dey said he needed time to confer with his advisers, and the Navy officers secured his promise for another audience on the morrow.

Back on Shaw's flagship, the commodore and Perry planned a quick course of action. By now, Great Britain and other powers were following the example of the Americans in demanding that the payment of tribute stop. Obviously if the Dey could wriggle out of his agreement with Decatur, he could maintain the golden flow of sea blackmail. With Decatur's forthrightness, Shaw and Perry agreed that the squadron should mount a warlike demonstration.

Next day, as the fleet was finishing preparations for action, Shaw sent Perry ashore under a truce flag with instructions to renew negotiations if possible. But now the Dey had a different argument. He blamed the Americans for violating the treaty terms in not returning the twenty-two-gun brig that Decatur had captured.

Angrily Perry denied the charge. America had relinquished all claim to the vessel, but as the Dey very well knew, the brig was now in Spanish hands. He must settle the matter with Spain. The crafty old politician held to his objection. He knew that since the treaty had now been considered at the highest government level in America, two Navy officers, however warlike, would not presume to set policy. Perry was checkmated.

Unhappily he agreed to continue pretreaty relations until new instructions could be obtained from Washington. Meanwhile, Shaler was permitted to return to his consulate quarters. More delay!

Ordinarily Perry would have been delighted with his assignment during the next two months as the squadron enjoyed the pleasant Mediterranean spring by visiting Syracuse, Messina and Palermo. But with his passion to return home, the leisurely cruise only made him more impatient.

Whenever he could, Perry sought out Americans aboard as the most reliable sources of intelligence. Now the Yankee traders in Sicily passed on word which he brought to Shaw. Possibly emboldened by Algeria's maneuvering, Tunis was showing hostility to America and again menacing United States commerce.

Shaw reacted with heart-warming decision. "We make sail immediately for the Bay of Tunis, gentlemen! Assemble there with gun ports dropped and decks cleared for action. We'll make it a show of strength."

Perry had one practical objection. He had not expected to have the *Java* out so long, and now her supplies were running low. Shaw snapped that it was imperative for every available ship to show at Tunis.

Then a twinkle flashed briefly in his stern eyes. Perry had confided to him his strange homesickness.

"From there, sir, you can proceed to Gibraltar to reprovision. You might find another ship there."

"The *Washington!*" Perry guessed.

"Aye, Captain Perry, with orders to the States. Good luck."

Curiously Perry asked if the commodore knew who had drawn command of the choice line-of-battle vessel, hoping it might be one of his friends.

"Oh, I thought you knew, sir. Commodore Isaac Chauncey. Matter of fact, he is coming out to take command of this squadron."

Chauncey his new squadron commander! Perry's heart sank. All too well he remembered Lake Erie and Steve Decatur's much more recent warning. *If I were you—and I don't think I'm exactly a timid man— I'd be most careful if ever I came under Chauncey's command again.*

Slowly he returned to the small boat waiting to take him back to the *Java*. No orders to the States now. Chauncey had him where he wanted him—a good, long distance from home.

"You all right, sir?" Jimmy asked anxiously as he came aboard.

Perry nodded reassuringly, and then Forrest hastened up, forgetting to salute. "I think you should know this at once, sir. I have just discovered that Heath has been corresponding with both Commodore Chauncey and Captain Elliott."

CHAPTER 20

THE moment the Big Rock loomed out of the purplish haze, Perry began bracing himself for his interview with Commodore Chauncey. He did not know what to expect. Presumably his protests over the way Chauncey doled out men and supplies to him at Lake Erie had long since been forgotten. But, as the court of inquiry had disclosed, Chauncey was still close to Elliott, and now there was the matter of Heath communicating with him.

As Gibraltar steadily towered higher and the *Java* made her harbor, Perry got his first look at the mighty *Washington*. She had been built less than two years before, with old Isaac Hull supervising the construction, and then masted under Macdonough's eye. This was his country's answer to foreign bullies!

A full line-of-battle ship, she measured 200 feet in length and 43 feet abeam, and her masts rose 180 feet. With gleaming black hull and twin yellow stripes that marked her two gun decks, the massive seventy-four gunner was a formidable sight. Perry felt a lump of pride in his throat.

As soon as the *Java* had anchored, Perry paid his compliments to his superior, and the meeting was strangely anticlimactic. Instead of the moody, aloof man he had known at Sackett's Harbor, Perry found Chauncey relaxed, friendly and hospitable.

"How pleasant to see you again, Oliver!" he exclaimed warmly. "I most deeply regret that I must detain the *Java* at this station, but let me explain the delicate situation that requires it."

Almost apologetically, certainly in far greater detail than a commander had to explain to a subordinate, he outlined his predicament.

Aside from the Barbary States, the Spanish were displaying hostility toward Americans. Only yesterday they'd had the presumption to threaten withholding of the squadron's provisions and stores until a duty was paid. He had further information that they now were collecting all their naval forces at Cartagena.

In all probability this massing of strength was inspired by the fact that the British had dispatched a large fleet to the Mediterranean. But surely Perry could understand why the *Java* must remain with the squadron. Most of the United States vessels had already left for home, and Chauncey, caught between two big naval powers, had only a frigate and two sloops to show the flag.

Perry was forced to agree. "I'm afraid, sir, we may have to have a showdown with Spain. Perhaps you haven't heard of the encounter between a number of our midshipmen from the Ontario and Spanish soldiers not too long ago?"

"Most interesting," Chauncey said. "What were the details?"

It had been something more than a casual shore-leave brawl, Perry said. One of the mids from Mr. Elliott's sloop—he tried to say the hated name casually—had been inhumanely butchered. He found it shocking that an American sailor could be murdered and mangled in the streets of a presumably friendly nation.

"If that is so, sir, we have fought to little purpose to acquire a standing that has astonished the world," he exclaimed. "Our honor will vanish as rapidly as it has been gained."

"Well spoken, sir!" Chauncey said warmly. "You remind me of what your friend Decatur said at a banquet for him in Norfolk. You wouldn't have heard it out here in the Mediterranean, but his toast is sweeping the nation. *'Our country! In her intercourse with foreign nations may she always be in the right, but our country, right or wrong'!*"

"That's Steve, all right," Perry said affectionately. "Perhaps put a bit too strongly, but I always told Steve he talks big."

Next, Chauncey wanted briefing on the diplomatic front. Shaw's show of force at Tunis had restored friendly relations there, Perry reported. But the Dey of Algiers was trying to wriggle out of the treaty. He still maintained the Americans had violated, and thus broken, the agreement reached with Decatur.

"In other words, sir, he proposes to revert to the original treaty by which we pay tribute, with one 'compromise,' and I tend to agree with him."

"What! Knuckle under to the beggar?"

"In lieu of money tribute, he now asks powder and shot," Perry explained. "I propose that we oblige—by burning the powder and firing the shot at the rascal."

Chauncey laughed. "That's more like you, Oliver. For a moment I was worried."

There was still another complication with the Dey. He was abusing Hugh McDonnell, the British consul, and again enslaving British subjects, even those who he had licensed to engage in coral fishing in Algerine waters.

Worse, in his lustful hate for Christian women, he was selling off European virgins on the slave markets for enormous sums and personally debasing them.

In one particularly shocking case, when a girl tried to defend herself against him, the Dey casually turned her over to his soldiers. After repeatedly using her, the soldiers left her naked in the streets, and the girl committed suicide by throwing herself into the sea.

"If that's what brought Lord Exmouth and the British fleet here, by God, sir, we ought to back them up!" Perry exclaimed.

Suddenly it was the old, familiar, timid Chauncey speaking. "Not so fast, Oliver! We mustn't be precipitate. I know the Dey wants Shaler removed, but he's still our best expert on Algerine affairs. Shaler insists we continue peaceful negotiations, and I feel it only prudent to take his advice."

Can the leopard change its spots? Perry thought disgustedly. Still buck passing and shilly-shallying and port-and-starboard tacking. Hell, it was July and with an indecisive commander like Chauncey, the *Java* wouldn't get home till winter!

But he restrained himself. "Yes, Commodore. May I now be permitted to return to the *Java?* I must see about provisioning her."

"Aye. And, Oliver, I am sure we will have most harmonious relationships."

With a fair wind that gave promise of good passage, the *Washington* and *Java* finally sailed from Gibraltar for Naples, but the comparatively short run dragged into a week's cruise. Restlessly pacing the quarterdeck, occasionally glancing aloft at the lookout, Perry waited for the first sight of the castle-studded heights surrounding the bay.

Despite his impatience, he had to loaf along with less than half his canvas drawing in deference to the slow progress of the *Washington.* A half-mile astern, the big ship had most of her sails furled so that apprentices could be put through station drills, and she lumbered at a maddeningly casual pace.

Perry halted his pacing at the *Java's* wheel and called for his glass from one of the two quartermasters now handling her. Again he studied the *Washington's* lines, and though she was holding him up, she was certainly a ship of awesome beauty.

"Land ho!"

The lookout's cry was repeated by a dozen voices back along the *Java's* glistening deck, and the officers sprang into action.

"Isle of Capri, sir," Forrest reported. Next, Yarnall mounted the ladder to report on the quarter-deck, followed by Macpherson. Briefly Perry studied the distant island through his glass and then checked the signal halyard of the *Washington.*

"Clap on full sail, Mr. Macpherson." He turned to the quartermaster. "Four points to larboard. And Mr. Macpherson, take her in under a full press of canvas and bring her about into the wind at anchorage."

On the *Washington,* he could see the tiny figures of topmen as they unfurled all sail, and her great towers of convas seemed to leap skyward.

"Mr. Yarnall, have the boatswain sound general quarters, sir. And assemble the guard and band."

"Aye, aye, sir."

Perry checked his laced hat and pulled at his tight cassimere pantaloons. We'll give Naples a good show, he promised himself.

Perry's young brother came on the quarter-deck to report the middies all on station.

"How goes it with you lads in the fo'c'slc?" Perry asked.

"Fine, sir," Jimmy said. And I want to thank you, sir, for inviting me to sup with you. I live high as a post captain, and I am grateful."

Perry's weathered face reddened slightly. "We are brothers first, Jimmy. You may be out here a long time."

"Aye, sir, and at an appropriate time, I'd like to talk with the captain about that, sir. I'd like to remain out here until I have something more to carry home than I brought out."

"Like Mull wine?" Perry inquired slyly. Forrest burst out laughing. The mids were always mixing batches of the fragrant wine for themselves. Looking embarrassed, young Jimmy saluted smartly and returned to his station.

"Band formed and ready, sir," Macpherson announced. "The guard commander requests permission to mount the quarter-deck."

Perry nodded and watched as the guard formed.

"Where's Heath?" Yarnall asked suddenly. "I can hear Lieutenant McCall shouting on deck, but not Heath."

"He said he was indisposed," Forrest reported, with emphasis on the word "said."

"Indisposed? Perry snapped. "Fetch him, Mr. Forrest! Then take your station, sir. Form the second division aft, Mr. Yarnall. Mr. Macpherson, you stay at the wheel."

Forrest and Yarnall, touching their caps, left. McCall came onto the quarter-deck and commenced dressing the ranks of the assembled marines. Up forward, seamen had taken their positions at the capstan, ready to lower away on the anchor.

After dressing the ranks, McCall reported formally to Perry, and the commander began his routine inspection. Most of the men were clean, though shabby. In Gibraltar, Perry had been unable to reuniform them as supplies had not arrived from the States and there was neither the time nor material to have them made at the Rock.

But several of the marines in the rear ranks were wearing dirty uniforms. One was so outrageously soiled that Perry flushed in anger. Just as he was finishing inspection, Heath came on deck.

Somehow, Perry controlled himself and spoke calmly. "Captain Heath, you will take your station."

"Very well, sir." Heath spoke indifferently. His voice was strangely thick, and there was the usual odor of wine on his breath.

Perry moved the hammock cloths, which had been neatly lashed down near the larboard rail, and stared blankly toward the distant heights of Naples. He counted to ten, then turned to Heath. "Mister, I was under the impression that I had specifically ordered that all marines were to have their uniforms in order for our entry into the Bay of Naples."

"Very well, sir," Heath repeated in the same tone.

He stood carelessly, feet apart and hands in pocket, his cap cocked on one side of his head. His coat was mussed, his trousers baggy at the knees. Macpherson, standing alongside Perry, was angry and the commodore restrained him with a gesture.

"Well, Mr. Heath, three men are wearing uniforms that are quite soiled, and one is a disgrace! You will have them removed from station, sir, and confined until punishment is determined."

"I think that would be unwise, sir," Heath said. "I told you at Malaga, Mahon, Algiers and Gibraltar that my men were in want of clothing."

Perry felt the blood rushing to his face. "Mr. Heath! I do not care for your manner. There is something unpleasant about it, and I suggest you remove it forthwith!"

"Very well, sir." Again the tone was maddeningly indifferent.

"A man in the dress of that marine," Perry said, his finger stabbing toward an offender, "is a disgrace to this ship and the Corps!"

"I reported the want of clothing," Heath said obstinately. " I cannot help it."

"Can't turn out the men to launder their own clothing!" Perry almost shouted.

"Laundering makes them fall to pieces, sir. They are best left dirty, but serviceable."

Damn this insolent dog, Perry thought. He stared at Heath a moment, then turned his back and walked slowly to the hammock cloths, bending over them to hide the rage on his features. He heard Heath directing Lieutenant McCall to have a corporal escort the offenders below so they could wash their uniforms.

As Heath took his position before his men, Perry slowly returned to stand alongside the red-faced Macpherson. "I've never seen a marine captain like him," the tall executive officer exclaimed. "It's almost as if he were deliberately trying to provoke you, sir."

Perry eyed him thoughtfully for a moment. "Take over, Mr. Macpherson."

"Aye, aye, sir." Macpherson touched his cap. Returning the salute, Perry moved aft to the taffrail where Tom Anderson was standing alone.

"By God, I'm a peaceful man, but I think there's one that deserves flogging!" the little diplomat blurted. "You ought to confine him to quarters and demand his removal."

"Perhaps, but we're reducing man power, and a tosspot like that can't expect to remain long in the service. Besides, he seems almost to invite removal, for some obscure reason, and I'd rather not oblige him. But I wonder why, Tom. Why?"

Thoughtfully Anderson studied the slouching figure of the marine officer.

"Mr. Heath has been fraternizing and drinking with his men so they have neither respect nor fear for him," he said slowly. "It's most puzzling."

"Violates the very spirit of the Corps!"

"And for that reason, Oliver, I think his actions deliberate. In other words, I think he's playing an underhanded game directed at you. Would he have reason, for example, to play the Judas sheep?"

The phrase coming from Anderson startled Perry. He had heard exactly the same words some months previously from Steve Decatur.

CHAPTER 21

AFTER Chauncey had collected his entire squadron at Naples, he ordered them on to Messina, a possibly unwise decision. Not only was the water bad in the squalid port city, but Messina's depraved dock women were notorious even through the Mediterranean. Venereal diseases were rampant, and from the officers of a schooner that had arrived earlier Yarnall and Doc Parsons learned that more than half the crew was sick.

On their advice Perry forbade all shore leave. Anyhow, the squadron would be moving on almost immediately for Tunis. President Madison had changed his mind after all about Tom Anderson. Withdrawing his nomination to have Anderson succeed Shaler at Algiers, the President instead had appointed him consul to the Regency of Tunis. Now Perry would deposit him there.

Perry worried about his men. Maybe it was because he had been too lax with Heath, but whatever the cause, the men were beginning to get out of hand, and he was determined to stop them.

However, Heath felt no obligation to set his men an example by refraining from shore leave in the forbidden city. He returned one night from a wild time ashore, complained that he was "indisposed" and retired to his stateroom. Not long afterward, a shore party from another vessel passed close by, and in response to calls of their tars, two of the *Java's* marines jumped overboard and swam ashore.

Perry was in his cabin at the time, but when the watch alerted them, his subordinates moved promptly.

Lieutenant Turner pursued the deserters in a small boat, and young Lieutenant McCall relieved him. He sent Midshipman Buchanan to notify Heath. The captain reported himself unwell and asked that Lieutenant Howle turn out the marines for him. As this was being done, Perry was informed, and hurried on deck.

Surprised at Heath's absence, he demanded to know the nature of his "illness," which none of his deck officers could explain. Midshipman Overton was sent to Heath's stateroom to tell him that Perry wanted him immediately. When he came on deck, Perry curtly ordered him to muster his men and determine how many were missing.

After some delay, Heath said in a surly fashion that the men were mustered but he still didn't know how many were missing. In all, it was almost twenty minutes before Heath finally made his report, and Perry suspected he was falsifying the muster roll to protect some absent favorites.

Once before, when Heath had openly ignored his orders about clean uniforms, Perry had threatened to replace him. Now he felt he'd had enough of Mr. Heath's insolence.

"Go below, sir!" he roared. "I have no further use for your services!"

He ordered a search party ashore and not two, but five marines from the *Java* were found in the forbidden city. Much as he detested flogging, Perry ordered thirty-nine lashes for each of the offenders.

When his wrath finally cooled, he wondered in his conscientious way if he had overtightened discipline. Perhaps brief shore leave would relax the men. He decided to find out firsthand whether Messina was as dangerous as Yarnall and Doc Parsons had reported. Two nights later he and Tom Anderson slipped ashore for an inspection.

It was worse than they had suspected. Though Perry considered himself reasonably tolerant, Messina's entertainments thoroughly disgusted him, and he decided he had been right in forbidding shore leaves. It was nearly eleven o'clock when they returned to the *Java*. As he was preparing for bed, he found a letter which had been left on his table during his absence.

Curiously he opened the envelope. As he read, he felt rage rising in him, and he reread it slowly, fighting vainly for self-control.

U. S. Frigate *Java*, Messina, September 18, 1816

Sir: On the evening of the 16th instant, I was ordered below by you, from the quarterdeck of this ship, with these words, or to this effect: I have no further use for your services on board this ship. I have waited until this moment to know why I have been thus treated, and being ignorant of the cause, request my arrest and charges.

Very respectfully, your obedient servant,
J. Heath, Captain Marines.

The cool insolence of the dog! Going to his cabin door, he roared to a startled marine guard to bring Captain Heath to him forthwith. When Heath came, Perry tried to keep his temper, but his words were loud enough to be overheard by Marine Corporal Philpot, the corporal of the guard, sitting on a match tub outside the door.

"How dare you, sir, have the assurance to write me such a letter!"

Shaking his head insolently, Heath said his feelings were concerned and that he had the right to know what charges were being lodged against him.

"Are you aware, sir, to whom you are speaking and where you are?" Perry demanded.

Coolly Heath said he was under the assumption that he was aboard the *Java* talking to Captain Perry.

"Be silent, sir!" Perry commanded. But Heath kept talking, deliberately baiting Perry, and now the captain could no longer restrain himself. "Sir, I am putting you under arrest!"

Perry called to Corporal Philpot to get him his sword and summon Marine Lieutenant Howle. When the young marine officer showed, Perry's face was livid.

"Sir, I have arrested this man! He has not only dared to write me an insulting letter, but he has insulted me in my cabin!"

Heath attempted to say something, and Perry roared, "Keep silent, sir, or I will have you put in irons!"

"Very well."

"If you repeat that again, I will knock you down!"

Heath smiled contemptuously. Levelly eyeing his superior, he said, "Very well."

Perry could no longer contain himself. His hard, weathered fist drove into the pudgy face that mocked him, and, with a surprised grunt, Heath collapsed. Perry stood lightly, hopefully, on the balls of his feet, but there was no fight in the fat figure still lying before him.

"Take him out and put him in irons," Perry said disgustedly to young Howle.

Silently Howle helped Heath get up and, taking him by the arm, led him to his stateroom. He returned to make sure that Perry wanted the prisoner in irons.

Already Perry's rage had subsided, and he was bitterly regretting his conduct. "No, lieutenant," he said tonelessly. "Confine him in his room and put a sentry over him."

Howle saluted and left.

"I'd say, Oliver, that the fat's surely in the fire now."

Perry started. In the excitement of the past quarter-hour, he had completely forgotten that Tom Anderson was a witness to the whole sorry mess.

"Yes, Oliver, every marine officer in the Mediterranean, and back home, too, will rush to the rascal's defense."

"How could I have done it, Tom! Completely unjustifiable."

"I wouldn't say that," the diplomat observed thoughtfully. "Heath has been asking for this. Deliberately so, I would say. If there is a court-martial or court of inquiry, or whatever you military fellows call it, I would be delighted to testify. Perhaps as an impartial civilian, my word might carry some weight."

"Thank you, Tom. I am afraid I may have to take you up on that. You would be a crucial witness for me in any investigation."

After a sleepless night Perry decided he must do one thing, much as it galled him—apologize to the bastard! Lieutenants Crane and Macpherson drafted the note for him and presented it to Heath. But the marine waved them aside. He preferred, he said, to rely "upon the laws of my country for justice."

By the time the squadron reached Tunis, the news had spread through all the vessels, and the men, officers and marines were sharply divided in their opinions of Perry and Heath. To complicate the situation, Captain Elliott came to fetch Tom Anderson, insisting that Commodore Chauncey was most anxious to get him safely landed ashore.

Perry was reluctant to surrender his star witness, but orders were orders. Anyhow, he calculated, Anderson would be close at hand if an inquiry were conducted promptly, as it should be.

Now, under the single, flickering flame of the only lighted shell lamp in his cabin, he held a council of war with his most trusted officers.

"I didn't see you strike him, sir," Yarnall said. "But I can understand it. Damned if I don't believe I'd have run the surly bastard through!"

Forrest's young face was troubled. "I figure Heath will demand a duel before he's satisfied, sir. Perhaps he means to kill you, or at least try. It's all part of the plot, sir. Captain Elliott is looking real smug these days."

"Aye, it all goes back to Erie and the *Niagara*," Yarnall agreed.

But it was the cool-headed Macpherson who put his finger on Perry's weak spot. "You've got damned few witnesses, sir. Heath's got numbers on his side."

"Aye, and the whole United States Marine Corps," Perry agreed wryly. "It's a proud outfit. That's why Tom Anderson is so important to me. He's my one unprejudiced witness to offset Heath and his lackeys."

His head resting against the paneled bulkhead, Doc Parson studied Perry with a professional air. "You're tired, sir, and the fever's coming back. You'd best rest. Tomorrow is soon enough."

"I'll try to sleep on it then, gentlemen," Perry said agreeably. "Now, if you will excuse me?"

But there was decision in his eyes, and the alert Macpherson lingered a moment after the other officers had filed out.

"The captain had best turn up that damned shell lamp if he's going to be writing anything," he said noncommittally. "It's a poor light at best, and hard on the eyes. Good night, sir."

Perry smiled faintly, said good night and closed the door. Quickly he went to his table and, dipping the quill point firmly, addressed a letter to Commodore Isaac Chauncey, Commander of the Mediterranean Squadron, Tunis Bay, Octover 8, 1816.

The decision made, he wrote steadily for a quarter of an hour, pausing only to dip his quill, as he described frankly "an event of a very unpleasant nature." He accused Heath of "palpable neglect of duty," "usual indolence and inattention to the calls of his office"—and yes, Perry thought, why not come right out and say it?

"The general deportment of Captain Heath towards me, so contrary to the usual address of my officers, and, moreover, his marked insolence to me in many instances, induced me to believe that his conduct proceeded from a premeditated determination to insult me on every occasion."

There, Commodore Chauncey, your Judas sheep has been doing his job!

When the marines had jumped overboard at Messina, he recalled, Heath first had pleaded "the subterfuge of indisposition" and then had mustered his men "in so careless and indifferent a manner" that Perry had been forced to send him below. At the showdown two nights later, Heath's manner was "so highly irritating and contemptuous" that Perry felt forced to arrest him. And, when he repeatedly ignored orders to remain silent, "I gave him a blow."

Frankly Perry expressed his mortification that he should have so far forgotten himself, "however improper his conduct might have been and however just the cause," and he pleaded only one simple justification.

"Frequent outrage added to frequent insult provoked this disagreeable consequence," he wrote.

Then, asking Chauncey to order a court of inquiry or court-martial as he might see fit, Perry made his closing.

"After eighteen years of important and arduous services in the cause of my country, it can hardly be imagined that I have any disposition to infringe that discipline which is the pride and ornament of the Navy; and to prevent any intention being falsely ascribed to me, I beg you will give immediate attention to this request, that the Navy, as well as my country, shall be satisfied of the integrity of my motives."

There! A bit wordy perhaps, but no time for polishing the phrases. He wanted the inquiry as soon as possible. He sealed the envelope, called Forrest, and directed that he take it to the *Washington* the following morning as soon as his division went off watch. For the first time in weeks, Perry slept soundly.

Perry was still eating breakfast the next day and teasing his brother Jimmy, when Forrest returned from the flagship. Chauncey, he reported, was about to issue orders for the squadron to make sail for Algiers.

Perry could guess the timid commodore's reasoning. "Now that Lord Exmouth has blown hell out of the city and palace," he explained to Forrest, "Chauncey can capitalize on it. The Dey, he figures, will now see the light. But we will have the inquiry before leaving, I assume?"

"No, sir." There was frustration and anger in the young officer's voice.

"Commodore Chauncey says, sir, that it is most likely he will put off the inquiry until such time as we get back to Port Mahon. And Lord knows how long that will be."

"Any delay favors Heath," Perry objected. Already, rumbles of quarter-deck despotism" were going through the squadron.

"Aye, and Elliott's schemings, too, sir. But those were the commodore's orders."

"Then we will be taking Tom Anderson along with us on the *Java*?"

Forrest avoided his superior's eyes. "I'm afraid not, sir. The Commodore says that Anderson is much too busy with affairs at Tunis. He cannot permit him to become involved in such a *trivial* matter as this."

"Trivial! The honor of one of his senior officers!"

"Those were his very words, sir."

Heath to Elliott to Chauncey, Perry thought slowly, the trap had been neatly sprung.

CHAPTER 22

BY NOW Oliver Hazard Perry was more than convinced that what Yarnall, Forrest, Sam Hambleton and Steve Decatur had been telling him from the beginning was right. There was a hidden but persistent plot to discredit him in the eyes of the officers and men of the United States Navy.

That night the message flashed by the *Washington's* signal lanterns was a confirmation. The whole squadron was to sail the next morning for Algeria. But why, Perry wondered.

Though Exmouth had humbled the Dey, Chauncey actually could not accomplish anything by another visit. He still had not received any answer from Washington to the Dey's letter written six months ago. More, the gusty, treacherous Mediterranean winter had arrived, and a levanter, whistling in from the northeast, was lashing the usually placid sea into mountainous, white-capped blue waves.

The only reason for the maneuver, Perry decided, was to separate him from Tom Anderson and further delay any proceedings by a court of inquiry. Naturally the men assumed that Perry was trying to stall the matter, and by his silence Chauncey tacitly confirmed the misapprehension.

During the rough passage, Forrest tumbled through an open gangway, into the sea, and only Perry's inspired seamanship, bringing the *Java* about in the teeth of the levanter, saved him. If it weren't for his youth, Perry thought, the exposure would have killed him.

At Algiers, Shaler, the American consul, came aboard the *Washington* to confer with the squadron officers. His report on Exmouth's bombardment corroborated the devastation that Perry had seen through his glass.

The British fleet had poured 30,000 shots and 300 shells into the city, crippling the Algerine navy and merchant marine, ruining the Dey's palace and destroying most of the houses. Including his own, Shaler added wryly. Whereupon, the Dey had seen the inhumanity of Christian slavery and ransom demands and had promised to reform.

However, without any direct orders from Washington, Chauncey could do nothing. With Shaler remaining aboard the *Washington*, the squadron made for Gibraltar to await dispatches from home. For two weeks they loafed there, then proceeded to Morocco and returned again to the Rock.

The senseless sailing, which only further delayed the inquiry and his own return to the States, made Perry edgy, and he was short-spoken even to his friends. "He could stand some relaxation ashore one of these nights," Sam Hambleton told Doc Parsons. "And don't you keep saying he needs rest, rest, rest."

But before Sam could persuade Perry to enjoy a night in the town, the schooner *Spark* arrived with the long-awaited instructions from home. Shaler and Chauncey were commissioned to settle with the Dey, once and for all, so again the squadron headed back to Algiers.

Chauncey planned to conduct the negotiations on his own quarterdeck. Then a northeaster howled in, and the fleet could not even run in to anchor. Shaler was put ashore with Charles O. Handy, acting chaplain of the *Java*, who was to become secretary of the American mission, and Chauncey led his quadron back to Port Mahon for reprovisioning.

Though they idled there a week, waiting for the weather to break, Chauncey still made no move to call an inquiry. Then, without giving Perry any inkling of his plans, he ordered the squadron back to Algiers.

Now the Dey tried to stall, pointing out with some justification that Washington had taken eight months and a day to answer his letter. The peace-minded Shaler was inclined to be tolerant of the Dey's position. He told Chauncey that a plot by religious fanatics was being mounted against the Dey, and the harassed ruler claimed that if he were forced to sign the treaty he would break it at the first opportunity.

But, backed up by Madison's orders and the example set by the brave Exmouth, Chauncey was unexpectedly courageous. He packed Shaler ashore with an open threat of war, and the Dey collapsed with a last, weak filibuster. After all, he pointed out, Friday was his Sabbath, Saturday the Sabbath of his Jewish interpreter and Sunday was Shaler's so the matter would have to wait until Monday.

The three holy days were too much for Chauncey, especially as new storms were blowing in. He left Shaler and Handy in Algiers, and instructed the *Spark* to wait there for the signed treaty. Then he took the rest of the squadron back to Port Mahon again.

Now it was almost New Year's 1817, and Forrest, Yarnall and Hambleton were standing near the poop on the quarter-deck of the anchored *Java*. The three were joking and wondering whether they could coax Perry ashore for a New Year's Eve celebration.

In the mutual exchange of good-natured insults, Macpherson quietly mounted the ladder and moved toward them.

Forrest saw him first, and touched his cap. "Why the sober look, sir?"

"I heard you talking about plans for a New Year's Eve party," he said slowly. "I'm afraid there won't be one. Commodore Chauncey has directed Captain Shaw to form a court for trial of such prisoners as may be brought before it."

"Trial of prisoners?" Forrest echoed. "That's odd language."

"Aye," agreed the tall first officer. "They plan to try Heath first on charges which, it has been decided, Captain Perry must bring."

"Damned clever," growled Yarnall, a frown clouding his face. "Makes him look like a martinet, preferring charges while this personal incident remains uncleared."

"What do you mean they'll try Heath first?" Hambleton asked, his voice suddenly suspicious.

"Wondered if any of you would catch that," Macpherson said sadly.

"You don't mean they're going to bring Oliver up on charges!" There was anguish in Sam's voice.

Macpherson angrily socked one fist into his other palm. "Exactly, gentlemen! Abusive and unwarrantable language to an inferior, and cruelty. Namely, striking an officer."

"It will break his heart if they hook him on this," Sam said. "It will."

He sighed. "Trouble is, the fool is a dedicated, devoted Christian. I've known him longer than any of you lads, and many's the time I've seen him on his knees. He turns the other cheek. He believes with the Bible about loving thy enemies and doing good to them that hate you."

"A rugged assignment," Yarnall grumbled, "and look at the mess it's gotten him into."

Despite his bitter complaints the night before that Perry needed more rest, Hannibal faithfully aroused him at dawn, as he had promised. It was the last day of 1816, and the first convening of the court, which was set for 10:00 A.M. Perry needed the intervening hours for final conferences with Macpherson, his first officer, and Lieutenant McCall.

Along with Marine Lieutenant Howle, Chauncey had directed that both naval officers must appear as witnesses. Perry had asked for Tom Anderson's appearance, too, but Chauncey waved aside the request. "The witnessing officers will be sufficient," he ruled.

At least, Perry grimly told Macpherson and McCall over breakfast, he had hit Heath with everything in the book. There would be three separate charges backed up by seven specifications, or incidents. By now, he reassured them, he was no forgiving dreamer, and he spelled out the charges almost happily.

"Disrespectful, insolent and contemptuous conduct to me, his superior officer . . ."

That involved Heath's conduct when Perry had challenged him about the soiled uniforms in Naples, his later letter in "highly improper" language demanding to know the charges against him, his "highly provoking and disrespectful" deportment in Perry's cabin at the showdown.

"Charge second. Neglect of duty and unofficerlike conduct . . ."

This covered Heath's remissness when the marines went overboard at Messina, his failure to report on deck when summoned, his careless mustering of the men, his lack of effort to recover the deserters.

Charge third. Disobedience of orders . . ."

Here, Perry explained, he was nailing Heath for his persistent refusal to keep silent in Perry's cabin, despite repeated orders to do so.

"All told, gentlemen, I am accusing Mr. Heath of having violated parts of the thirteenth, fourteenth, fifteenth, twentieth and twenty-eighth Articles of the rules and regulations 'for the better government of the Navy of the United States.' I didn't want this to happen, but by God, I intend to see it through!"

Even to a veteran officer like Perry, the members of the court were an awesome group as they were smartly piped aboard the *Java* and assembled, in dress uniforms with swords, to open the inquiry.

With trim-bearded Captain Shaw, president of the court, was Master Commandant R. S. Kearney, a doctor and judge advocate for the proceedings. Also sitting on the board were five captains: William Montgomery Crane, John Orde Creighton, John Downes, Thomas

Gamble and H. B. Breckenridge; two Master Commandants, William Hall and George W. Rodgers, and Marine Major John Hall.

Though the court had planned to open promptly at ten o'clock, Doc Parsons delayed the austere gentlemen by obstinately insisting that he be allowed to remain in the cabin because Perry needed medical attention. The fever was kicking up again, and Doc finally persuaded Dr. Kearney to let him stay.

Then Heath was ordered in to state whether he had objection to any member of the court. "No, sir," he said to Shaw.

At a nod from the court president, the clerk arose, shuffled papers, nervously cleared his throat and began reading the charges.

As the clerk droned through the repetitious legal verbiage that sounded like a civilian indictment, Perry studied the individual members of the board.

He relied on Shaw implicitly to conduct a fair trial. He did not know Downes very well, but the captain had distinguished himself at Tripoli and again as commander of the brig *Epervier* when Decatur humbled the Dey at Algiers. Further, Steve had later transferred him to his own flagship, the *Guerrière*, and that was reference enough for Perry.

His eye caught that of Master Commandant George Washington Rodgers, and he almost laughed outright. Not only had Rodgers commanded the *Firefly* under Decatur—he also happened to be Perry's brother-in-law, having married Anna Marie Perry.

But three members of the board had him worried. Marine Major Hall most likely would sympathize with Heath. Then there were captains Crane and Creighton, who had a great deal in common with Mr. Elliott. With him they had been aboard the *Chesapeake* when Barron struck so ignominiously to the *Leopard*.

Not bad for the Chauncey-Elliott-Heath cabal. They were starting with at least three, and possibly more, of the ten-man board on their side.

As the clerk finished the reading and quickly sat down, Shaw looked toward Heath. "How do you plead to these charges, Mr. Heath?"

"Not guilty, sir."

"Proceed to trial," Shaw rumbled, nodding to the marine guard at the door. "Bring in the witnesses, sergeant."

Macpherson, McCall and Howle were sworn in together, but the latter two were then ordered to withdraw during Macpherson's testimony.

The first officer could testify only to Heath's conduct when Perry had reproached him in Naples about the soiled uniforms. As Perry had expected, Marine Lieutenant Hall was quick to question if Heath had been disrespectful and insolent.

Macpherson held his ground. "His manner of reply to Captain Perry was, I thought, very disrespectful."

In sharper tone Hall demanded to know what Heath had said, and what his conduct had been.

"He came up to Captain Perry—he had his hands in his pockets and his hat a little on one side of his head—with a swagger." He demonstrated. But he admitted that he could not distinctly recall Heath's words.

Now Master Commandant Hall intervened with a question, and Perry chalked up a fourth sympathizer for Heath.

"Isn't Captain Heath in the habit of wearing his hat on one side, and keeping his hands in his pockets?"

So far as the hat, yes, Macpherson answered. "But I cannot say that I have observed that he has the habit of carrying his hands in his pockets."

Shaw told Perry he could now interrogate Macpherson. Perry had only two questions.

First, hadn't Captain Heath previously said to him that if the marines were dirty, he couldn't help it?

"I recollect that Captain Heath used that reply to Captain Perry."

"Was the marine, although in worn-out clothes, clean in compliance with the orders that had been issued?"

"No," Macpherson said decidedly, "he was not."

"That is the extent of my questioning, sir."

Shaw directed Heath to question if he cared. Cleverly the captain forced Macpherson to admit that Heath had made many protestations that he never intended disrespect to Perry. "Which I was bound to believe," Macpherson added honestly.

But, in his eagerness, Heath overpressed his point by asking the same question again.

"I have heard Captain Heath *say* so," Macpherson answered.

His face flushing at the implication, Heath demanded angrily: "Have you not frequently heard me say that I used every exertion to please Captain Perry in the discharge of my duty?"

Macpherson smiled tightly. "I have heard Captain Heath *say* that

155

there was no man in the Navy he would sooner please than Captain Perry. That he regretted exceedingly what happened. I heard him say so *since* his arrest. Captain Heath has always spoken in favor of Captain Perry—as have all of the other officers of the ship."

Good man, Perry thought gratefully. Hurriedly Heath ended his examination.

Next, when Lieutenant McCall described the escape of the two marines overboard, Marine Major Hall displayed a lively interest. Was Heath on sick list, he wanted to know. "He came from shore, said he was unwell and turned in," McCall answered.

Master Commandant Rodgers expressed surprise over Heath's absence ashore and his supposed indisposition. "He had been absent from the ship," McCall replied. "I did not know that he was unwell until he mentioned it."

A point that will be amplified later, Perry said grimly to himself.

"Did you know the nature of his indisposition?" Downes asked suspiciously. No, McCall said.

Had he appeared unable to attend to his duties because of it? "I think he might have got up sooner," McCall said firmly.

Quickly Marine Major Hall made the young lieutenant concede that Heath had generally paid proper attention to his marines. Further, could McCall say whether the captain had received a direct order to pursue the fugitives? McCall couldn't say.

Shaw looked inquiringly at Perry. By now Perry could feel the fever reaching his eyes, and he said tiredly, "No questions."

Heath demanded to know whether he had been dilatory in mustering his marines.

"I heard Captain Heath hurrying up the sergeant. I heard him three or four times tell him to bear a hand."

Rashly Major Hall tried to develop this promising lead. "Was Captain Heath prompt and active on the occasion?"

McCall answered bluntly, "Not very."

Despite his dizziness, Perry knew he had to nail the point down. "Did Captain Heath attend to the marines *at all* until directed to do so by me?"

He believed not, McCall answered.

It was young Howle who proved the surprising witness, but Perry supposed that he felt a duty to his own Corps, and he couldn't blame Howle too much.

Yes, he had seen Heath's letter to Captain Perry, but he couldn't pass on the merits. "I presume it will be laid before the court, which is better able to judge."

Rodgers questioned him on the time element of Heath's appearance on deck after being ordered up by Perry.

"In a few minutes. In a very short time, for a man who was in bed and had to dress himself."

Even allowing for Corps loyalty, that's a bit thick, Perry thought.

Captain Gamble broke his silence. Perry knew that he was the son of a Revolutionary major and suspected he would have scant sympathy for an insolent malingerer. With one question, he confirmed Perry's hopes.

Had Heath attempted to muster his men and determine who were absent *before* Perry directed him to do so. Howle evaded a direct answer.

"The marines got on deck nearly as soon as Captain Heath got there. He was in conversation with Captain Perry when I came up."

Gamble appeared ready to pursue this tack, as Perry wanted, but Major Hall intervened hastily. "Did Captain Heath make those exertions that the occasion called for?" he asked sharply.

Perry almost felt sorry for the witness. A young marine lieutenant being questioned by a marine major about a marine captain. He accurately predicted the answer.

"As far as was in his power, I suppose he did. There was no delay in getting the marines on deck. I had them on deck as soon as Captain Heath got there."

"You have stated," Gamble intervened again, "that Captain Heath ate supper after he came aboard. Did he eat heartily?"

"I did not observe what he ate."

"Did Captain Heath report his case to the surgeon?"

"I don't know." Somewhat unnecessarily he added, "I don't know whether the surgeon was on board."

Perry heard Doc Parsons' half-suppressed snort of annoyance.

Howle gave an accurate account of being summoned to Perry's cabin, of hearing an interchange between his two superiors, of seeing Perry floor Heath. But, he said, he did not consider Heath's tone contemptuous. Had the captain's language and manners been respectful or disrespectful, Major Hall asked.

Howle paused a moment. Then he said slowly, "I did not conceive them disrespectful. The only words I heard him say were 'Very well.' His gestures I did not observe."

With this clear defense of Heath, seven bells sounded and Captain Shaw ordered adjournment for the day. Perry rose as the board filed out, then walked uncertainly to the table and sat down. Cradling his head on one arm, he fell into an exhausted sleep.

CHAPTER 23

NEW YEAR'S DAY 1817 arrived with a northeaster that set the taut, tarred rigging of the *Java* to shrieking. Before the sullen dawn broke, Perry was on deck to study the weather.

"Levanter bearing down on us again," he said to Yarnall.

The big officer nodded. "Bet the lads on the *Spark* are having a rough time at Algiers. That harbor's rough as a cob, anyway."

Perry's fever had almost disappeared, and, as Doc Parsons came from below, he greeted him cheerfully. "None of your tea, Doc. I'm feeling fine. Something else on my mind, though."

Parsons gave him a quick professional appraisal, seemed satisfied and then said, "I can guess. Whether Heath was on the sick list? Well, he wasn't."

"I'll ask you to testify, Doc."

"Aye, and it should be brought out that you were sicker than Heath ever has been, to my recollection."

"No, not that. Let's just stick to the record."

"Howle was called to the *Washington* last night," the surgeon observed. "Says Elliott was there. I wonder where Howle stands, anyway?"

Perry didn't answer. He had misgivings himself after listening to the young marine lieutenant's testimony the previous day.

"I think he's going to be all right," Yarnall said slowly. "I know he has no use for Heath."

When the court-martial was resumed, Yarnall's prediction was borne out.

Under questioning by Heath, the lieutenant said he had received orders through a midshipman, not from Heath, to recover the marines who had gone overboard. Heath flushed angrily.

"Was I careless and indifferent in mustering the marines after I came on deck?"

"I did not perceive that you were careless about it," Howle said. "After you were done with Captain Perry, you spoke to and hurried the sergeant." His emphasis on the word "after" was unmistakable.

Heath quickly concluded his questioning, and Doc Parsons was called as the next witness.

When he testified that Heath had not been on sick list, the defendant's fat face quivered in rage. "He complained to me the following morning of a slight indisposition," Doc went on. "But he did not report himself to me on the evening of the sixteenth of September."

Clenching his fists nervously, Heath demanded, "Have I ever endeavored to evade my duty by feigning indisposition or alleging as an excuse the subterfuge of being sick?"

"I do not recollect that Captain Heath ever feigned indisposition," Doc replied, faint sarcasm in his voice. "He was always actually indisposed when he applied for my assistance."

Heath abandoned the attack and unexpectedly asked Captain Shaw for permission to recall Lieutenant Macpherson. Shaw glanced inquiringly at Perry. No objections, Perry said.

The *Java's* executive officer, looking in bewilderment at both Perry and Heath, returned to the witness chair. A scowl on his face, Heath recalled Macpherson's testimony that he had been disrespectful to Perry in their discussion about the men's dirty uniforms.

"Was my manner also contemptuous or insulting?"

"Yes," Macpherson said bluntly.

Surprisingly this seemed the answer that Heath had wanted. Eagerly he moved a step closer to the witness. For the record, he made Macpherson admit that Perry had not followed up the incident with arrest or suspension. Then he elicited that Macpherson had served under Perry nine years before in New York, later on Lake Ontario and, finally, for the past fifteen months as his first lieutenant on the *Java*.

Neither Perry nor the witness could understand what Heath was leading up to until he triumphantly demanded: "And from the knowledge you have of Captain Perry's character, and his rules and system of discipline, do you think he could suffer any officer under his command to treat him in a disrespectful, insolent and contemptuous manner, without an immediate arrest or suspension from duty, or otherwise notice it?"

The legalistic trap had been too neatly constructed for a man of

Heath's intellect, Perry surmised. Someone, probably aboard the *Washington*, had coached him well.

But Macpherson, hesitating only a moment, was ready. "I have never known an instance—but the present," he said calmly.

Things weren't going so well today for Mr. Heath, Perry thought, and smiled quickly at Doc Parsons sitting alongside him.

Captain Shaw asked whether Heath wished to call any further witnesses. Taking a piece of paper from his pants pocket, Heath said he would like to recall Lieutenant McCall, then question Midshipman Buchanan and Overton, Marine Corporal Philpot and Marine John Coleman.

He returned the paper to his pocket, casually leaving his hand in the pocket, too. Perry saw Captain Shaw's eyes narrow in annoyance.

The baby-faced midshipmen, who merely had served as messengers to Heath in his cabin, gave quick, frightened testimony, then scuttled off the stand with sidewise glances at Perry. He nodded encouragingly to them.

In reciting the events that had led up to Heath's arrest, both the marines spoke as though they had been rehearsed. Doc Parsons leaned over to whisper, "Someone did some figuring last night." However, their testimony was merely a general confirmation of what had previously come out, and, to Heath's discomfiture, questioning by the court produced two strong new points in Perry's favor.

At first, as Captain Shaw prodded Corporal Philpot about details of Perry's conversation with Heath, Perry couldn't understand what he was driving at. Then Shaw asked how long Heath had been in his superior's cabin.

"I'd say about ten to fifteen minutes, sir."

Perry saw the point. Shaw was demonstrating to the court that Perry's actions had not been abrupt—it had taken time for Heath to anger him.

When the other marine, Coleman, was called, he explained that he had been on post at Perry's cabin door. He quickly agreed with Heath that he had seen nothing disrespectful, insolent or contemptuous in his conduct toward Perry.

Suddenly Master Commandant Rodgers interjected an unexpected question, and Perry blessed his brother-in-law.

"Was there any other person in the cabin besides Captain Perry and Captain Heath at the time you heard somebody ordered to be put in irons?"

"There was another person besides," Coleman said slowly. "He came on board with the captain that night."

Perry sensed the stir of interest among the board members, and Rodgers cast a puzzled glance toward him. Perry remained expressionless. The groundwork had been unwittingly laid by Heath's own man, and at the proper time, Perry would make the point that his best witness was unavailable.

Shortly before the trial resumed Thursday morning, Captain Shaw visited Perry. Did he want Heath "drummed out of the service, or just given a slap across the bobstay," he bluntly asked. Shaw made clear that he was acting in an official capacity, not showing any partiality toward Perry.

"I want to know, just in the event the court finds Heath guilty," he explained. "It is for my own information."

Despite his disclaimer, Perry reasoned, he would not have asked the question if he at least were not convinced of Heath's guilt. But he hastily assured that he didn't want the man cashiered.

"He made me angry, captain, and I regret it. But I don't really regret striking him, I'm afraid. I think that perhaps a strong reprimand might straighten him out."

Quizzically Shaw studied Perry. "Are you going to tell me the whole story?"

"Whole story?"

"Aye. What's behind this damned thing? I mean what are the things that won't emerge at the inquiry?"

Perry thought a moment. "I'd rather not go into it, sir. It's a long, complicated, unnecessary part of this proceeding." He sighed. "The sail's been sheeted home. Let's let it alone."

Shaw thumped the table heavily, and rose. "Very well, captain. Promptly at ten, then. What are your plans?"

Perry said that, after offering a simple statement, he would present himself for questioning by the board and also by Heath.

"You needn't, you know."

"I would prefer it that way, sir. I think courtesy demands it."

When court convened, Perry was called immediately. He rose, straightened his uniform, and walked slowly to the witness chair, but remained standing.

In more than eighteen years of naval service, he said, he never before had acted as a court-martial prosecutor and Captain Heath was the first marine officer with whom he ever had any difficulty.

Shaw interrupted gently. "The court understands your position, sir. But you will first be sworn and then you may continue."

Perry blushed. In his eagerness to tell his story, he had forgotten. He was quickly sworn, and continued.

At Naples, he recalled, Heath's manner had been "indecorous and unbecoming." When the marines went overboard at Messina, there had been considerable delay in getting Heath's report, he said, contradicting young Howle's testimony.

"It was from fifteen to twenty minutes, at least, after I got on deck and after I had given the order to muster the marines, that I obtained the report, a length of time which I deemed altogether unnecessary."

At their final confrontation in Perry's cabin, Heath's manner "was irritating in the highest degree, both in person and in looks." His tone was "insulting," his smile "contemptuous." Then, to underscore his most serious charge of disobedience, Perry told the court with emphatic warmth: "I arrested, and repeatedly ordered him to be silent. He continued to reply until he was taken out of the cabin, and all my efforts to make him keep silence were ineffectual!"

Perry turned expectantly to the board for their questions.

Quickly Marine Major Hall wanted to know about Heath's smile, his tone faintly indicating that Perry was perhaps overly sensitive.

Perry fixed the major with a cold stare. "He had a sardonic grin on his face, and a contemptuous look."

Hall seemed about to ask another question, but then thought better of it.

"Was any other person in the cabin at the time?" Captain Shaw asked innocently.

Good old Shaw! He wasn't going to let Tom Anderson's absence pass unnoticed.

"Mr. Anderson, the consul at Tunis, was present." As the board members looked at him with lively curiosity, Perry paused a moment for effect.

Then, quietly but forcefully, he added: *"He is a very material witness in the case, and I regret very much that I cannot have the benefit of his testimony."*

Shaw let Perry's words sink in. "If there are no more questions," he said finally, "Captain Heath may now question the witness."

Perry sat down, staring coldly at Heath. The marine avoided his eyes as he asked why Perry had not promptly arrested or suspended him when he thought his conduct merited it.

"I object to the question," Perry snapped.

To the board, he recalled that he had testified to his patience on many occasions with Heath, and therefore he would leave it to them to decide the question's propriety. Shaw had the cabin cleared for a conference, and then recalled Perry and Heath. The board agreed with Captain Perry.

Perry returned to the witness chair and turned to address the board. He had objected, he said, because the question was irrelevant, but he was glad to answer it voluntarily.

"I did not arrest or suspend Captain Heath at the time because of a reluctance to do such to any officer when there was a possibility to avoid it."

Heath looked surprised, but resumed his questioning. "Have you any reason to question my veracity?" he said in wounded tones.

Perry answered shortly that he must have had some. After all, when Heath was presumably ill in his cabin, his name did not appear on the sick list.

"This is the universal custom of the service and of this ship," he snapped, "and I am entitled to the services of all of my men and officers who are not so reported."

Perry felt his anger rising, and reminded himself he must not let Heath bait him into a display of temper before his fellow officers.

"What do you perceive in the letter I addressed to you, requesting an investigation of my conduct, to be either improper or reprehensible?"

"I have already expressed my entire disapprobation of the letter."

"Do you not think that every officer, when labouring under a suspension of duty, and conscious himself that he is injured, has a right to request an investigation of his conduct?"

"At a suitable time," Perry said shortly.

Under Heath's clever questioning, he did have to admit the marine had assured him he had no intention of insulting Perry. "But your conduct was so much at variance with your assurances that I paid no attention to them," he added.

Heath concluded and, at his request, the proceedings were put over an extra day, until Saturday the fourth, so that he could prepare his defense. Though Heath had had little else to do for months, Perry did not offer any objection.

CHAPTER 24

"I LITTLE expected, on leaving my native country, that I should be arraigned before a public tribunal. . . . I will not waste the time of this court in needless declamation or unnecessary digressions, but shall aim at the vindication of my character and conduct, to rescue which from imputation of a charge, I submit to your consideration a few remarks. . . ."

For almost a quarter of an hour, the whining voice extended the few remarks. Heath was making his defense summation at the final session of the court, and the longer he listened to the pretentious rigmarole, the happier Perry felt.

Surely this impossible creature must disgust the board, as he did Perry. Studying their stony expressions, he concluded that he was right.

"I remained below for two days, under feelings the most mortifying —I felt no longer able to bear the indignity which I conceived in the manner attached in sending me below. . . .

"On approaching Captain Perry, I received harsh and improper language. I felt conscious that I did not deserve such treatment. I was thunderstruck for a moment! I was at a loss to know whether the scene before me was real or imaginary! . . ."

Grimly Perry listened as the lies poured out. Heath had always sought to have his marines "appear as respectable as possible," had always considered his manner to Perry "respectful and polite," had never for a moment intended to convey the opposite impression.

Pompously he described his wounded sensibilities when Perry summoned him to his cabin for the showdown.

"My character, which is dearer to me than life, assaulted, and every weapon of defense interdicted! Can this be suffered! Nature herself revolts at it! She will not endure that all the finest and noblest feelings, the sublimest portion of her ethereal spirit, be thus rudely violated! . . ."

Finally, sweat streaming down his fat face, Heath was done. "Whatever, then, may be the determination of this court, from the proud consciousness of my innocence I shall derive consolation."

Banging his gavel in relief, Captain Shaw ordered the court cleared so the board could go over the record with Dr. Kearney, the judge advocate.

For more than an hour, Perry stood at the *Java's* taffrail, staring vacantly across the choppy waters of Port Mahon. Finally he and Heath were recalled. Both stood stiffly at attention as Captain Shaw read slowly from a paper on the desk.

"The court, after mature deliberation on the testimony adduced, and having weighed and considered the whole matter, together with what the prisoner had to offer in his defense, agree that the charges are in part proven."

With difficulty Perry suppressed a look of relief. Heath seemed to sag and then, as Shaw spelled out the various convictions, his face turned greenish. He was exonerated of neglect of duty and unofficerlike conduct in the incident of the absent marines, and the court acquitted him of having used highly improper language to Perry.

Otherwise, on two out of the three charges, on four of the seven specifications, he was guilty as Perry had alleged. The sentence, Shaw concluded, would be a private reprimand from the president of the court.

As the board adjourned, Shaw also directed that the clerk send a copy of the decision immediately to Commodore Chauncey. Heath was about to leave when Shaw called him sharply. "You will remain, please, Mr. Heath. I have a few things I want to say to you."

The old sea dog had an angry glint in his eyes, and Perry concluded that he would execute sentence of the court with considerable satisfaction.

It was a week and a day later that Perry's own court-martial began. In contrast to the gales which had ushered in the new year, there was now clear weather and just the hint of a southwesterly breeze.

With Hannibal making frequent trips up and down the steerage ladder to fetch special tidbits from his cabin, Perry was visiting sick crewmen. He heard the boatswain's pipe, and came up to find that Captain Shaw had arrived early.

"Do you always attend personally to the sick men in steerage, sir?" Shaw asked curiously.

"Aye, John."

"Then that was hogwash that Heath gave us last week. Testified that

165

you didn't receive a report from the surgeon on every case of sickness, didn't he?"

"I ought to know, sir," Doc Parsons interrupted. "The captain gets a morning and evening sickness report, sir. Heath knows damned well that Captain Perry keeps himself carefully informed."

Shaw nodded thoughtfully. "I can't help feeling there's more to this than just a hitting incident. Hell, I've belayed a couple of officers in my time."

He looked curiously at Perry.

"It's almost as if Commodore Chauncey himself were after you, Ollie."

"There is more to it, sir," Parsons said eagerly, but Perry silenced him.

"What do you mean about Chauncey, captain?"

"He was so startled when we presented the court's decision to him. Signed it without comment. And Heath acted mad as hell, as if he hadn't expected Chauncey would accept it."

Shaw looked inquiringly toward Doc Parsons, but, under Perry's frown, the surgeon kept grumpily silent.

As the proceedings opened, Perry felt the preliminary symptoms of a feverish attack. He mustn't collapse, he thought. He mustn't. No one but Doc Parsons would believe that he wasn't using sickness as a pretext to delay the court-martial.

Standing at rigid attention, he heard himself accused of "ungentlemanly and unofficer-like conduct" in the language he had used to Heath and "oppression and cruelty" in having struck him.

"How do you plead, sir?" Shaw asked courteously.

"Not guilty!"

Perry's plan had been to present Tom Anderson as his star witness, along with Marine Lieutenant Howle, the two Marine guards, Philpot and Coleman, and Captain Heath himself. However, Heath demanded his fellow Marines as prosecution witnesses, and Perry offered no objection.

Howle was the first to testify. "I was in the wardroom on the evening of the day specified in the charge, and was lying in my cot directly under the cabin," he began. Then he went on to tell the details. He had heard loud talking, and had heard the captain say he wanted to see him. So he got his clothes on and went into the cabin, to see Captain Perry and Captain Heath in conversation, standing by the after gun in the forward cabin. As he opened the door, he had heard Heath say something about feelings, and then he had heard Perry order Heath to be quiet.

As soon as Howle entered the room, Perry had turned to him, he recalled, and announced that he had placed Heath under arrest. Perry had also said he felt inclined to have Heath put in irons, for Heath had not only written him an insulting letter but had insulted him in his cabin.

Howle testified then that Perry had turned to Heath and asked if Heath did not think it would serve him right to be put in irons. Heath had answered only, "Very well, sir," according to Howle's recollection.

Then Perry had turned wrathful. He had shaken his fist at Heath, and he had warned the Marine captain not to repeat that insolence, or he would knock him down.

Heath repeated the words. Perry struck him, and then Howle got between them.

Perry called for his sword, but Howle gestured to the others who had entered the cabin that he was not to have it. Perry then ordered Howle to take Heath below and put him in irons. Howle started out with the prisoner. He stopped at the hatchway to the wardroom, and looked back inquiringly. Did Captain Perry really want him to put Heath in irons?

Perry had calmed a little then, and said no, but to put Heath in his stateroom and place a sentry over him. He did so.

A little later Captain Perry had called for Howle, the Marine said, and asked him to write down the circumstances as they had occurred, since Perry was sure the matter would not end there. When Howle left the cabin, he asked what orders he should give the sentry he had put before Captain Heath's cabin. Perry had said to remove the sentry, but to tell Heath he was confined to quarters. The next morning Captain Perry had told Howle to let Heath use the wardroom.

It was obvious, as the testimony showed, that Perry had been greatly angered, but had then slowly cooled down.

Corporal Philpot, who had not seen the incident, had heard Perry call for his sword, and had been present during part of the altercation. He so testified again.

Lieutenant McCall had seen nothing. He had been in bed at the time of the incident. John Coleman had heard Perry calling for his sword, and ordering someone in double irons. But he had not known what the fuss was all about until he saw Lieutenant Howle come out of the Perry cabin leading Captain Heath. Coleman was the sentry on duty at the cabin door at the time of the argument.

Perry sat silently through all this repetitious testimony. The only difference would come when Heath took the stand. Perry did not know what he would do, or how he would do it, but he was quite certain of one thing: Heath's testimony as to the same set of facts would be quite different this time from that during his own trial.

And so it was. Heath's memory seemed to have improved remarkably in a single week.

Heath recalled that he had been ordered below by Captain Perry on the sixteenth of the month. Perry had told him he had no more use for Heath's services aboard the ship. Then, after two days below, Heath had written to Captain Perry, requesting that he be placed under formal arrest and that charges be made against him. He was anxious, Heath informed the court solemnly, to know the cause of his suspension from duty.

Perry watched. In every word, in every gesture, Heath was playing the part of a wronged, innocent man. And Perry grimaced. Heath now pretended he had not known the cause of his captain's anger—Heath, who had comported himself as a disgrace to the Marine Corps, who had spoken insolently and rudely at every turn, who had made every move possible calculated to insult and infuriate the captain of the ship!

Now Heath recalled that in Perry's cabin, in "harsh and irritating" language, Perry had told him angrily, "You damned rascal, you have insulted me. It was not my intention to have arrested you, but I will now work you for it!"

Perry, he went on, continued his abusive language. "The precise words I do not recollect except those of 'rascal' and 'scoundrel' which were repeated. I replied, 'Very well, sir.' . . .

"Captain Perry now advanced toward me, and to the best of my recollection, with his fist clenched, saying, 'If you repeat those words again, I will knock you down.' Seeing Captain Perry advancing toward me in this manner, I immediately replied, 'Captain Perry! Don't strike me!' I think it was nearly the same instant I received a blow from him."

Neatly done, Perry thought morosely, very neatly done. Heath had managed to make him out an overbearing bully. When the whining voice concluded, he quickly decided against cross-examining Heath. With the fever coming on, he feared, he might lose his temper all over again if the wretch stuck to his lies.

Instead, he submitted to the court copies of the letter in which he described the incident to Chauncey and of his personal apology which Heath had rejected. Then, very briefly, he addressed the court.

He emphasized the unfortunate absence of Tom Anderson . . . the prosecution's advantage in having testimony by corporals and privates "to distort and mangle circumstances and language imperfectly seen or heard" . . . Heath's rejection of his apology ("too favorable an opportunity to give his commander trouble to let pass.")

Proudly he squared his shoulders and looked the court, one by one, squarely in the eye.

"I ask if it is possible that I could in mere wantonness commit an act of violence? No, gentlemen! It was the outrageous conduct of this officer that produced the consequences that resulted."

The fever now was burning in him and his voice faltered. "I will therefore leave my case in your hands."

Faithful Doc Parsons at his side, he slowly left so the court could deliberate. "Guilty," he said to the surgeon. "Might as well face it. The bastard has finally run me aground. And it hurts like hell, Doc! A mar on a perfect record."

When they were called back, the unhappy look on Captain Shaw's face confirmed Perry's prediction. The defendant was guilty "in part" on both charges. However, in view of his attempted apology, the court deemed that he should receive only a private reprimand from his commander in chief—Chauncey.

From a distance, it seemed, he heard Shaw still speaking. ". . . and he is hereby sentenced accordingly." Parsons quickly grabbed his arm as Perry swayed, helped him remain on his feet till the board had filed out.

Then he slumped into a chair, and the last thing he remembered clearly was the triumphant face of Captain Heath as the Marine paused at the door to stare back toward him.

Yet that was not the end of it. The case aroused immense interest in the entire squadron. Chauncey, of course, took a sly delight in the opportunity to keelhaul his young rival—for that is how Chauncey considered the man who was only eight names below him on the seniority list.

The officers of the unit split according to rank. The junior officers, without knowing the facts, sided with Heath. Conditions in the American Navy were hard. The relationship between junior and senior officers had not yet been clarified and, in a republican Navy, unlike a Royal navy, there *were* certain differences. Americans, even young ones in inferior office, were more conscious of their rights as citizens than their opposite numbers in the British navy might have been.

Many of these young officers knew little about Captain Heath and cared less. It was the principle of the thing they were interested in. There was no doubt that Perry, a ship's captain, had struck Heath, the commandant of Marines on the *Java*. That was all these hotheads needed. They were judge and prosecutor both. They sent a memorial to the Senate, calling on that body to witness that they no longer had any guarantees of safety of their own persons, and asked that the Senate reopen the entire case.

Chauncey's other captains were shocked. They sent their own memorial to Chauncey, asking that he forward it to the Secretary of the Navy. They asked that the men who had signed the memorial to the Senate be relieved of command. And the senior officers pointed out, quite rightly, that their juniors had upset all tradition by appealing directly to the legislature, claiming that they were oppressed by their commanders. The captains said they believed these men might mutiny if left aboard their ships.

Even Chauncey agreed that the insubordinate ones should be relieved of duty and sent back to the United States as quickly as possible. Obviously the Perry-Heath case was going to become one of the *causes célèbres* of the United States Navy, and Oliver Hazard Perry was not to hear the end of it yet.

CHAPTER 25

AT LAST! It was spring at home in Newport, and Perry busied himself as much as he could with simple family matters: the boys—three of them now, Oliver, Grant and Raymond; the accounts that Elizabeth had tangled in his absence; the prolific mare who seemed always to be foaling.

But mostly he tried to tease Elizabeth out of her worry; there were circles of anxiety under her eyes, and she worried constantly over the Heath controversy. For, despite the two courts-martial, the ugly business would not die.

Heath, having been forced out of the Marine Corps, was pamphleteering and politicking to stir up further trouble for Perry. Only yesterday, the harassed Navy officer had felt it necessary to write a rather strong letter to his superior, Secretary Crowninshield.

Heath's supporters were preparing a petition for submission to the United States Senate, attacking Perry and his court-martial board, and Heath had asked Crowninshield to make Perry yield some of the records.

Referring to "the late Captain Heath," Perry wrote to Crowninshield: "I am induced, Sir, to believe that some sinister object is intended by his request, and duty to those gentlemen who are now absent and to myself compels me to withhold my consent to the papers being placed in the hands of one who, I am sensible, will make an improper use of them."

"Isn't that rather strong, Ollie?" Elizabeth asked doubtfully.

"Mayhaps. I will add a sentence softening the effect." He inked his quill, then slowly wrote, "Permit me, Sir, to return my thanks to you for the delicacy which you have shown me on this occasion."

In a separate letter he enclosed a message of support from the officers of the *Java*, noting that "*they* have not been guilty of that spirit of insubordination. . . ." To Rodgers, who forwarded a copy of Heath's pamphlet to him, Perry could express himself more freely. Heath, he wrote back, was a "detestable fellow" and "destitute of truth, of honor and of spirit." But, more than by Heath's "infamous falsehoods," Perry was worried by the shockingly lax discipline throughout the Navy.

"This calls loudly for the notice of officers of rank and standing," he told Rodgers. "Let me charge you, my dear Sir, while your attention is directed to preparing ships of a superior description, you do not neglect the inquiry, 'how are those vessels to be officered.'"

When Sam Hambleton wrote from the South, where he was visiting, Perry answered with a chatty, affectionate letter. "My horse family increases almost too rapidly," he confided. "The mare has had another colt by Duroc and is again in a fair way. Young Oscar is a beauty and promises to make an elegant saddle horse. He is said to have all the points of a runner and is larger than we expected."

He could not keep the controversy out of his mind, though. While he had been planning to go to Washington, he told Sam, he was now undecided because of the Southern attitude on the Heath affair.

"Your Southern gentry have treated me with so little consideration that I shall remain with those who know me and wait until my service is wanted," he wrote irritably. "When it is profitable, they may change their tune. I mean those who have thought it such a terrible offence to chastize an impertinent and insolent blackguard."

But the blackguard had wealthy and influential friends. James Monroe, the new, strong-willed President, went out of his way to show respect for Perry, naming him his special aide during an inspection trip of the Eastern harbors.

None the less, Congressmen debated, newspapers editorialized and Heath brazenly challenged Perry to a duel.

Finally, just a year after the court-martial, Perry made his decision. Despite his strong feelings against the barbaric practice, only a duel would silence the dispute once and for all—and thus, perhaps, help a little to restore discipline in the Navy. He wrote Steve Decatur, asking him to serve as his second.

Steve was delighted—till he read Perry's curious stipulation. Thereafter, as the arrangements dragged on for months to the accompaniment of publicity, he worried day and night that he was arranging only for his friend's murder.

Heath's supporters stirred up so much agitation about the affair of honor that Perry suspected they were more interested in the publicity than their principal's "satisfaction." And for a man presumably sorely aggrieved, Heath seemed content that authorities all over the country were on the alert to prevent the meeting.

Early in October, accompanied by his second, Lieutenant Desha, Heath came up to Rhode Island. Strangely, publicity accompanied them, too, and both were taken into custody until they agreed to keep the peace and leave the state.

But now Perry was determined to nail down his elusive challenger. Before Heath and Desha departed, secret arrangements were completed for a meeting on the tenth near Washington. There was a dueling ground at Bladensburg in a deep ravine somberly called Valley of Chance.

Perry went further. He made a declaration that, in giving Heath satisfaction, he was only atoning for his violation of service rules in hitting him. He was not giving any consideration to the claims Heath had been making. These he denied. To make sure his position was completely clear, he had the two seconds, Decatur and Desha, sign the paper.

But again there was delay. Somehow, Decatur passed Perry on the road to Washington, and had to turn back to New York. Finally it was agreed the pair would meet at high noon above Hoboken on the Jersey shore of the Hudson River nine days later.

During the bumpy carriage ride from the small tavern to the dueling grounds, Perry and Major James Hamilton chatted casually about the weather, the fall colors that had richly stained the Jersey countryside, all other topics except the most important.

Steve Decatur remained obstinately silent. He looked sympathetically at his friend. After almost two years of the incessant controversy, Perry's face was haggard, his temples touched with gray. It would be good to be done with—but the way Ollie wanted it, he was inviting death.

Steve wondered if he should not have refused his friend in the very beginning. If anything happened, he'd have Ollie's blood on his hands.

At the level, grassy plain where so much blood had been spilled, the three passengers alighted, and the driver discreetly took the carriage into a grove of trees some distance away. If gentlemen cared to kill each other, it was no concern of his so long as the fare was paid and he didn't see what was going on.

Heath and Desha had not yet arrived.

"I still say you should reconsider, Ollie," Decatur said slowly. "Shoot the rascal!"

Perry's jaw set stubbornly. "I'll not argue about it any more."

Decatur shrugged. "What goes on in the mind of a man with such honor?" he demanded of Major Hamilton. "In twenty minutes from now, he proposes to expose himself to his bitterest enemy without raising his hand in self-defense!"

His fierce eyes narrowed. "If anything happens, I'll never forgive Heath."

"You are my second, sir, and the choice is yours in that respect," Perry said quickly. "But I would remind you again—I wish no harm to come to Heath."

"Two years of hell this conniving bastard has given you. Why, he's so bad he even turned on Chauncey."

"Typical of him," Hamilton said. "Probably figures it was Chauncey who forced him out of the Corps."

"Aye," Decatur agreed. "And if Ollie would shoot the dog down, it would be a favor to the Navy, the Marines and himself. For then maybe Mr. Elliott would shorten sail—as he's done before."

Not long before, capitalizing on the Heath controversy, Elliott had again raked up the Lake Erie dispute. In a letter to Perry he had accused him of "base, false and malicious reports" and offered an insolent suggestion. Perry should write privately to Navy Secretary Crowninshield urging that Elliott receive half honors for the Erie victory!

Perry answered so witheringly that Elliott, like Heath, demanded personal satisfaction. Instead, at Steve Decatur's suggestion, Perry prepared charges against Elliott, forwarding affidavits from Lieutenants Turner, Stevens and Champlin, along with one from Doc Parsons, to Washington.

"Should you be able to exculpate yourself from these charges," he coldly notified his former second-in-command, "you will then have the right to assume the tone of a gentleman. And, whatever my opinion of you may be, I shall not have the least disposition to dispute that right, in respect to any claim you may then think proper to make upon me."

Now, he thought as he waited for Heath and Desha, after today's business, if he survived it, there might well be another meeting with Elliott!

Shortly before noon his antagonist and second showed up, and Hamilton wasted no time in getting the business under way. He produced and checked a brace of big Navy pistols. Heath was given his choice by Perry, and then Hamilton placed the duelists back to back.

With Decatur and Desha he stood aside as he calmly recited the rules. At the count of three, each principal would advance five paces at measured step, wheel and fire when ready.

Though malevolence gleamed in Heath's close-set eyes, his face was grayish, and his mouth sagged down so the teeth showed. He seemed both eager and frightened, and Decatur saw that his hand holding the pistol muzzle down was shaking. He shifted his glance to Perry.

Apparently serene, Perry winked at Decatur and grinned slightly at the big man's worried expression.

"Ready, gentlemen?"

Hamilton's voice was clear and commanding.

"Ready," Perry said loudly.

Heath managed only an affirmative nod.

"*One!*"

The distant reaches of Lake Erie suddenly came back to Perry, and he could hear the roar of the carronades, could see Yarnall's bloodied, fighting face before him.

"*Two!*"

Well, anyhow, his affairs were in order. Decatur would look after the details if he fell.

"*Three!*"

Heath would try to shoot him in the stomach. There was no curing of such a shot, and it was a slow death, too.

Perry took measured deliberate steps. One step, and he offered a quick prayer.

Two steps.

Dear Father, forgive this man John Heath as I am trying to forgive him.

Three steps.

And, Father, if I fall here, look after my family. The boys are good lads, but so young. And Elizabeth—dear Elizabeth! I have worried her overmuch with my vanity and fighting.

Four, now five steps.

Deliberately he turned. He saw Heath's pistol, wavering as it sought his middle. Suddenly the muzzle belched a flash and a roar.

Perry had a fleeting impression of Decatur's face, tense and pale, and of Hamilton, leaning slightly forward.

He felt his stomach muscles tighten, waiting for the ball's impact.

But there was no impact. He stared down, looking for the blood, and then toward Heath. The devil had missed!

Heath recoiled, then toed his mark, his pudgy jowls working in fear. Naked panic showed in his eyes as he glanced first toward Perry, then imploringly toward Decatur.

Perry gripped his pistol hard, and his hand went sweaty. He continued to hold it muzzle down without firing.

Slowly, so slowly that it must have been an eternity to Heath, Decatur now extracted from his pocket the letter Perry had written him back in January. He measured five forward paces and turned to face Heath. He read the date, January eighteenth, and the salutation, "My dear Commodore."

"You are already acquainted with the unfortunate affair which has taken place between Captain Heath and myself," he went on in a level voice.

"Although I consider, from the course he has thought proper to pursue, that I am absolved from all accountability to him, yet, as I did in a moment of irritation produced by strong provocation, raise my hand against a person honored with a commission, I have determined, upon mature reflection—" Decatur paused momentarily to glance scornfully at Heath's glistening face—"declaring at the same time that I cannot consent to return his fire, as the meeting, on my part, will be entirely as an atonement for the violated rules of the service."

Ignoring the relief that suddenly lighted Heath's face, he went on. "I request, therefore, my dear sir, that you will act as my friend on this occasion. Very truly your friend. O. H. Perry."

Deliberately Decatur folded the letter and tucked it back into his pocket. Then he turned to Lieutenant Desha. "I presume, gentlemen, that the party claiming to be aggrieved is now satisfied?"

For a moment something murderous blazed in Decatur's eyes, despite his even tone. He braced himself, as though hoping that Heath would turn down Perry's gesture.

Quickly Desha moved to Heath, still standing at his mark, and there was a short whispered conference. Then he announced formally, "Captain Heath feels that his injury is atoned for."

Hamilton, Perry and Decatur returned to the inn in the same carriage. "Well, that's done!" Perry sighed in relief. "I'm glad it's over with!"

Decatur was less jubilant. "You should have shot the dog, Ollie. Mr. Elliott may become very brave now. He'll be wanting more than just your reputation."

CHAPTER 26

IT WAS their first meeting, and instantly Oliver Perry knew that he liked President Monroe's new Secretary of the Navy, who had several months previously succeeded Crowninshield.

Smith Thompson came from Dutchess County, the lush Dutch countryside of New York State where the patroons had settled along the Hudson River. He was a formidable legal scholar, having studied the law under Chancellor James Kent at Poughkeepsie in his native county, and an able public servant.

But he preferred the bench to politics, declining the mayoralty of New York City to serve in the state courts. When Monroe brought him to Washington, he was chief justice of his state.

Perry had come to see him in New York in response to a cryptically worded message. Now, the Secretary was offering him a secret assignment of the highest diplomatic importance.

America looked sympathetically on South America's struggles for liberty and wanted to maintain the friendship of their fiery Simon Bolivar. But President Monroe was determined to stop the plundering of American vessels by Venezuelan pirates, and at the President's suggestion, Secretary Thompson was entrusting the delicate task to Perry.

Perry could take several vessels, which might impress the Venezuelans, and anchor at their capital, Angostura. Somewhat vaguely, Thompson described Angostura as a city of about 10,000, located a considerable distance up a river known as the Orinoco.

Once Perry had found the mosquito-ridden place and located either Bolivar or his vice-president, Don Francisco Antonio Zea, he would be on his own. He would, however, enjoy the services of an accredited confidential agent to Venezuela, who could brief him fully on the government and its officials.

"I am honored that the President has chosen me, sir," Perry said simply. "I will do my best not to fail."

Thompson chuckled dryly. "The President—and I—have the fullest confidence you will not give up your ships, captain."

Quickly Perry made his plans. He would use the *Constellation* as his flagship, but since the frigate wasn't ready for a long sea voyage, he would go ahead in the sloop *John Adams*. Lieutenant Alexander Craxton, a good man who had served under Perry on the *Lawrence*, would accompany him in the schooner *Nonesuch*. When she was ready, the *Constellation* could follow.

His arrangements in order, Perry went to Washington for conferences with the State Department and paid a surprise visit to Steve Decatur at his handsome new home. As they sat out in the garden patio, Perry excitedly told him about his good luck.

But Decatur's face was sober, and Perry thought impatiently, Why does he throw cold water on everything I do?

"You've never been to Angostura, Ollie?" Decatur said finally.

Perry shook his head. "Why?"

"Well, it's on the slope of a hill up the Orinoco River—about three hundred miles up, as a matter of fact. Quite a stink hole. Millions of flies and mosquitoes and gnats, heat, dirt—and all kinds of fever."

"Aye, so that's it! Fever."

"Precisely. Even you have never really known fever till you get it in

Orinoco, Ollie. It's bad enough on a man who's never suffered from it
—let alone a chronic case like you."

Perry knew his friend had a point, but he was reluctant to admit it.

"Best back out," Decatur pressed him. "It's a dreadful risk."

"I'll concede I've had a feeling that if a bad fever should strike me
again, I wouldn't survive." Perry shrugged fatalistically. "But that's a
risk we all take, Steve."

"A damned unnecessary one at this point! Plenty of other officers
could handle it with considerably less personal jeopardy. Where did
your orders come from, anyhow?"

"Thompson wrote me from New York summoning me. Wouldn't
tell me what it was by post, though. Everything is highly confidential."

Decatur looked strangely at his friend. "And where is Mr. Elliott
now?"

"New York, I think."

"And Chauncey has had the Brooklyn Navy Yard for almost a year
now. Odd coincidence, isn't it? How did your name come to be suggested?"

Perry laughed. "Come off it, Steve! Surely you're not hinting this is
part of the plot?"

"Not so far as Smith Thompson is concerned," Decatur said. "He's a
fine man. But he's a civilian, after all, and rather new on the job. Somebody could have got his ear."

"Don't forget Thompson said the assignment came from the President himself."

Decatur wasn't entirely satisfied. He bit off the end of a long, slim
cigar and thoughtfully lighted it. "Still say you shouldn't accept," he
said bluntly.

"Well, there's extra compensation from the State Department,"
Perry argued. "You know I need the money. And—well, I'm sick and
tired of hearing how these South American pirates fatten on our commerce. It's almost the Barbary business all over again!"

Decatur sighed heavily. "I figured in the end it was probably your
damn devotion to country. Look here, Ollie! You've done more than
enough. Let Claxton or Turner, or someone like them, take the job."

"I'm going," Perry said stubbornly. "That's it!"

Theoretically Perry was to leave immediately, but days dragged on
as the State Department completed the diplomatic side of the arrange-

ments. It was the first week in June 1819 before Perry was able to obtain his final instructions from Secretary of State John Quincy Adams and he was actually ready to go.

Saying good-by to Steve Decatur, he found his friend again in a gloomy mood. Barron, who had struck the *Chesapeake* so ignominiously, was clamoring for reinstatement. Decatur thought his two fellow Navy Commissioners were inclined to let bygones be bygones, but he would oppose Barron to the end.

"Mr. Elliott is in this, too," he growled. "That fellow has his nose everywhere."

"Well, he was a middie under Barron on the *Chesapeake*," Perry said. "If Barron were cleared, his own position would be better."

"Aye, but there's a little more to it than that. I was on the court that suspended Barron for five years, you know. And young Mr. Elliott rebutted testimony on one of the main charges—a charge that could have got Barron shot."

Decatur rose and walked over to the locked, elegantly carved desk that stood in his living room. He tapped it lightly. "Speaking of Mr. Elliott, I have your papers against him safely secured inside."

Perry was startled. "No wonder I haven't heard from the Secretary about the charges. What are you doing with them?"

President Monroe had been studying them, Decatur explained, preparatory to any action. Decatur had taken them, he said, because he didn't want the new Secretary, Thompson, to see them before he could brief him orally.

"After all, they're pretty late in being filed."

"Aye, Steve, but I explain that."

Another thing, Decatur said. Perry was leaving for foreign waters, and many of the material witnesses were now posted to the Mediterranean Station. In their absence Elliott was sure to be vindicated.

"Think it over, Ollie. I don't want you getting involved in a mess that could only hurt you and the Navy."

"I suppose you're right, Steve. And I don't want to be vengeful about it. If anything should happen to me down in South America, forget the papers."

Decatur frowned. "I don't like the thought, but if it should, I'll forget them. Provided Elliott stops his damn whining."

"Agreed, Steve."

From Decatur's home Perry went directly to Annapolis, where he was joined by Irvine, the confidential agent assigned by the government, and Charles Handy, his former secretary now serving as purser for the expedition.

The following morning the *John Adams* weighed anchor and stood down the bay. By evening, they had rendezvoused with the *Nonesuch* and were standing seaward.

At supper, as he sat down to a steaming meal prepared by the faithful Hannibal, Perry imagined he felt the first faint signs of the recurrent fever. For a moment apprehension stirred deeply within him.

Then Dan Turner, his first officer, entered. Dan had commanded the brig *Caledonia* under him at Erie and served with Perry on the *Java*. He had a way of making people laugh, and now he made some offhand remark. Perry laughed and forgot his foreboding.

Descending the latitudes slowly, harried intermittently by head winds and calms, the *John Adams* and *Nonesuch* had a dull, wearisome voyage. Finally they reached an area where the wind hauled to the south and west under dark skies, indicating the approach of the hurricane season.

However, Perry knew, the storms never blew further than two degrees beyond Barbados, and he made quickly for that British port. After taking on provisions, the sloop and schooner proceeded to Port of Spain in Trinidad, and then on to the Orinoco's delta.

There was considerable difficulty locating the river's navigable mouth, and then the *John Adams* could not get over the bar. Perry transferred to the *Nonesuch*, and headed upstream, while the sloop turned back to Port of Spain.

For a full two hundred miles of their tedious ascent, the countryside—low, marshy and in places a great inland sea—was uninhabited. It was the most exotic scenery Perry had ever seen, but the beauty did not compensate for the tropical discomforts.

The nights were nightmares of mosquitoes, sand flies, gnats and other insects, and the crewmen shut up in their airless berths suffered bites by the hundreds. They rose in the morning, already exhausted by the moist, stifling heat, to work under an insufferably blazing sun. When the schooner worked close in to shore, there was some shade from the great trees, but the insects were even worse. To fight them off the men huddled in the strong smoke of burning oakum and tar.

At last, after eleven days, the *Nonesuch* dropped anchor in Angostura, fired the customary salute and sent an officer ashore to wait on government officials. President Bolivar was away with the army, and after welcoming the Americans hospitably, Don Francisco Zea, the vice-president, made it plain that he was in no hurry to conduct negotiations.

Perry took the delay as philosophically as his fever and native impatience would permit. From Irvine he knew that Zea was involved in a precarious power struggle at the moment with General Juan Bautista Arismendi, a Venezuelan national hero. Though a favorite of the Liberator and a former prisoner of the Spanish, Zea suffered the political disadvantage of having been Colombian born.

While Zea and Arismendi concentrated on their private political quarrel, Perry took up residence with Dr. Forsythe, an American, who was serving as his interpreter. It was a chance to get some rest, but the fetid Angostura made him uneasy. It was a sickly town. Creoles were dying by the score and, while the American party waited for Zea's ear, two Englishmen died.

Then the officers and crew of the *Nonesuch* began coming down with fever, and Perry wrote in his notes: "I must own there is something more appalling in the shape of death in a fever than in the form of a cannon ball."

As his own fever grew, he felt his will power being slowly sapped. In his mind he kept returning morbidly to the injustice of the court-martial he had suffered, Elliott's constant intriguing, Heath's wild lies about him. Adding to his troubles was Zea's cooler and cooler attitude.

At first Perry had liked Don Francisco, a revolutionist, botanist, scientist, editor and man of action. But, gradually, Perry noticed, perhaps under influential pressure, Zea began to believe the Yankees were interested only in reclaiming United States property that had been illegally captured.

"These people," Perry wrote testily in his notes, "affect to think that it is very unkind in the United States to demand restitution of any property, however piratically obtained, if it has been done in the name of patriotism."

He saw that tact and patience, two virtues which he had never possessed in abundance, were now supremely important to his mission. It was a relief to express himself in the safe privacy of his notes, and he continued writing angrily.

"Some difficulty may be anticipated in regulating their privateers by suitable restrictions, as people engaged in this business are the only moneyed men and, of course, possess great influence. They will not readily give up so fruitful a source of revenue as the privilege of plundering at pleasure the peaceful commerce of all nations."

But, with the help of Irvine and Dr. Forsythe, he maintained his firm, friendly attitude during the negotiations, and after three stifling weeks in Angostura, he was rewarded.

Somewhat reluctantly the Venezuelan Secretary of State conceded the principle of restitution. He promised that his government would effect an early settlement of its obligations and that Venezuelan cruisers and privateers would stop molesting American commerce.

Victory won, Perry wanted to leave the pestilent capital at once. Two of his lieutenants, Claxton and Salter, had come down with the fever, along with twenty of his crewmen. Fortunately Dr. Morgan, the ship's surgeon, assured him the disease remained nonvirulent and the men were recovering.

Though every instinct told Perry to weigh anchor immediately, there were diplomatic complications. The Venezuelan surrender came on a Wednesday, along with an invitation to Perry to remain another three days for a dinner in his honor on Saturday. He felt that to decline would revive all of Zea's suspicions.

After accepting, he found that on the Sunday following his reception, the republic's new constitution was to be proclaimed with religious ceremonies and enthusiastic cannon fire. Another delay! It would be unforgivable to leave before the ceremonies.

So it was Sunday afternoon before the *Nonesuch* weighed anchor at last and headed downstream. With strong, favoring currents, the passage was mercifully swift in contrast with the slow upstream journey. By Tuesday night she reached the Orinoco's mouth, and Perry tried to work her across the bar.

But the wind was from a poor quarter, and he finally decided it would be more prudent to anchor overnight and try again in the morning. Completely exhausted, he threw himself down in the trunk-cabin berth and fell into a deep sleep.

During the night the wind freshened sharply, and a rising sea smashed against the schooner's stern. Spray spattered down the companion hatch of the trunk cabin, thoroughly wetting Perry. When he awoke at daybreak, he was chilled. Worse, as he shivered uncontrollably, he recognized new symptoms, and sent for Dr. Forsythe.

The physician, who had taken passage back to the states on the *Nonesuch*, listened gravely to Perry's complaints. A fierce headache, back pains, very hot skin, muscular soreness . . . He consulted the regular ship's surgeon, Dr. Morgan, who was ill himself, and their diagnoses coincided.

Perry had contracted yellow fever in addition to his chronic fever.

With cathartics and surgical lancet, Forsythe worked for hours over his tossing patient. But the technique which had been successful with other cases aboard the schooner did not help Perry.

As Perry sank, Claxton desperately forced the *Nonesuch* across the bar in spite of continued ill winds and clapped on full sail for Port of Spain. In the trunk-cabin berth, Perry stirred fretfully, his mind wandering back over the years as the dreaded crisis approached.

CHAPTER 27

In the trunk cabin of the *Nonesuch*, Claxton and Dr. Forsythe waited, half hopefully, half in dread, for the crisis.

"Hope the *Constellation* will be at Port of Spain," the physician whispered. "She'd give him an easier, faster voyage home."

Perry half-raised himself from his berth. "Aye, the *Constellation!*" His eyes were fever-bright. "Served on her as a lieutenant . . . under Captain Campbell, Mediterranean-bound." He tossed uncomfortably. "Arrived off Tripoli . . . in September . . ."

The surgeon cast a puzzled glance at Claxton.

"His mind is wandering," the lieutenant said. "He's going back a good fifteen years."

By the fourth day the *Nonesuch* was still forty miles from Port of Spain, and progress was slow.

Maybe, Claxton decided, the *John Adams* might come part way to meet them. He dispatched an officer and oarsmen in an open boat to notify Turner of Perry's condition.

Though his strength was spent, Perry had lucid moments. Now, in a suddenly clear voice, he called to Dr. Forsythe. "Am I dying, sir?"

Uneasily Forsythe looked down at his patient. Perry's dark eyes seemed almost black because of the darkening of the skin around them.

"Bear up, Commodore," the surgeon said evasively. "We are near the *Adams*."

The eyes searched Forsythe's face, and Perry knew. "Aye," he said simply. "Few persons have greater inducements to make them wish to live than I. . . . But I am perfectly ready to go if it pleases the Almighty to take me. . . ." He rested a moment. "The debt of nature must be paid," he added abruptly, then fell silent.

On Monday, August 23, the *Nonesuch* raised the oncoming *John Adams*. The wind was dead, and while the sloop was still six miles away, Dan Turner, Purser Handy and Dr. Osborne, the *Adams* surgeon, left her in a small boat. They boarded the *Nonesuch* about noon.

Perry opened his eyes to see Turner's weather-beaten face looking down at him. He extended a feverish hand. Turner took it firmly, matter-of-factly, and then suddenly he choked.

"Bear up, Dan. The wind will change to a better quarter in time."

"Aye, aye, sir."

Perry's voice was weak, but he wanted to shake hands with Handy, too, and ask how he had been.

"Well, sir. I'm sorry, sir!"

"Fear not," the fading voice said. "Yea, though I walk . . . through . . . the . . . valley . . ."

He seemed to sleep.

"The crisis," Dr. Osborne whispered.

Helplessly they watched. Perry's skin turned increasingly yellowish. His breath, at first troubled and uncertain, then quickened and became shallow.

Seven bells sounded. Three-thirty.

Suddenly Osborne's eyes narrowed. Quickly he knelt beside the still figure, feeling for a pulse. Then, slowly, he passed his small surgeon's mirror back and forth across the mouth and under the nose. He got up and faced the others.

"He is gone," he said.

EPILOGUE

MIGHT one hope that the retribution of fate would strike down Perry's enemies, even after his death? Unfortunately, life was not so just. Isaac Chauncey went on to become one of three post-captains who made up a Board of Navy Commissioners and advised with the Secretary of the Navy in administering the Navy from 1821 to 1824. From 1825 to 1832 Chauncey commanded the New York Navy Yard. In 1832 he returned to Washington as a Navy commissioner, and served in that capacity until his death in 1840. In these last years he was president of the board—in other words, he held the highest post a career officer could occupy in the peacetime navy.

Jesse Elliott's career was more speckled, yet successful. Until 1822 he served as a captain and member of a commission appointed to select permanent sites for navy yards and fortifications. From 1825 to 1827 he served in the *Cyane* at sea, and was offered a post as admiral of the Brazilian navy, a job he refused. From 1829 to 1832 he was in command of the West Indian Squadron, assisted in suppressing a slave insurrection in Virginia, and represented the Navy in the nullification troubles at Charleston, South Carolina.

In 1833 Elliott went to Boston to command the Navy Yard there. In 1835 he was so well regarded that the Navy sent him to command the Mediterranean Squadron, engaged in those years on good-will visits to European nations. But if he was successful with the courts of Europe, Elliott was not successful with his men. On arrival home in 1838, thirteen of his disgruntled officers preferred charges against him, and he was convicted of misdemeanors. His friends said he was convicted because Andrew Jackson, his friend, had gone out of office and been replaced by Martin Van Buren. Always, Elliott's fate was bound up in politics of one kind or another.

Elliott was lucky in one way. Although the court convicted him of unseemly conduct in his last tour and sentenced him to suspension from the Navy for four years—two without pay—President Van Buren remitted the pay penalty.

Elliott's fighting with his enemies went on. James Fenimore Cooper published a history of the Navy which contained an account of the Battle of Lake Erie that was quite favorable to Elliott. The controversy broke out again. Perry's defenders attacked, and Cooper wrote a defense of Elliott that pleased the Commodore so much he ordered a silver medal made to honor Cooper. The medals were widely circulated, but some, like the Rhode Island Historical Society, refused to accept the medals, even as gifts.

Commodore David Porter was so enraged with Elliott's conduct that he challenged Elliott to a duel, but the duel was never fought. Besides arguing and writing in those days, Elliott retired to a farm to raise sheep and hogs. Then, in 1843, President Tyler restored him to active duty and, in December 1844, he was made commander of the Philadelphia Navy Yard. A year later he, too, died.

The controversy over the Battle of Lake Erie did not die, though. It was to continue for years, until the objectivity of time brought a considered judgment by naval historians. That judgment was the same as Perry's: Elliott had not served his Navy or his commander well by hanging outside the fighting at Erie, and letting Perry's flagship be shot to pieces.

History has been kinder to Oliver Hazard Perry and his memory than life or the Navy ever were. Nearly a century and a half have passed since the Battle of Lake Erie and the tumultuous career of this great seaman and fighter. But, in that period the names of Chauncey and Elliott have sunk into dimness, while the name of Oliver Hazard Perry has been raised to the glory he earned so well. And as for Captain Heath, that willing instrument of a will-o'-the-wisp fate, he passed from the pages of history with his service as an American consul in the Mediterranean. Of them all, outside the pages of musty histories, only the name of Oliver Hazard Perry lives on.

THE PERRY MEDAL

"He was buried at Port [of] Spain, Trinidad, with military honors. His death produced a most profound sensation throughout the United States, for it was regarded as a great public calamity. Tributes of national grief were displayed, and the Congress of the United States made a liberal provision for his family, and his mother, who was dependent on him for support. In 1826 his remains were conveyed from Trinidad to Newport in the sloop-of-war *Lexington*, and landed on the 27th of November. On Monday (December 4th) following he was interred with funeral honors due to his rank. His coffin rested in a sort of *catafalco*, the lower part being in the form of a boat. The canopy was decorated with stars and trimmed with black curtains, and at each corner were black plumes. The State of Rhode Island afterward caused to be erected a substantial granite monument to his memory. It stands upon a grassy mound on the west side of the Island and Cemetery, and at the base rest the remains of the commodore and the deceased of his family."

BENSON LOSSING, *Pictorial Field Book of the War of 1812*
(Harpers, 1869)

BIBLIOGRAPHY

Bancroft, George. *History of the Battle of Lake Erie and Miscellaneous Papers.* New York: R. Boyner's Sons, 1891.

————. *Oliver Hazard Perry and The Battle of Lake Erie.* Newport, R. I.: Mercury Publishing Co., 1912.

Barnes, James. *The Hero of Lake Erie.* New York: D. Appleton & Co., 1898.

Brown, Arthur W. *The Spirit of Oliver Hazard Perry and His "Men of Iron."* Providence, R. I.: Wm. R. Brown Co., 1928.

Burgess, Tristram. *Battle of Lake Erie with notices of Commodore Elliott's conduct in that engagement.* Philadelphia: W. Marshall & Co., 1839.

Cooper, James F. *The Battle of Lake Erie.* Cooperstown N. Y.: H & F. Phinney, 1843.

Crosby, Ralph M. *We Have Met the Enemy.* Indianapolis: The Bobbs-Merrill Co., 1940.

Dawson, Moses. *A Historical Narrative of the Civil and Military Service of William Henry Harrison.* Cincinnati: M. Dawson, 1824.

Dobbins, Wm. W. *The Battle of Lake Erie.* Erie, Pa.: Ashby Publishing Co., 1929.

Dutton, Chas. J. *Oliver Hazard Perry.* New York and Toronto: Longman, Green & Co., 1935

Fenton, Alfred H. *Oliver Hazard Perry.* New York and Toronto: Farrar & Rinehart Inc., 1944.

Griffis, Wm. Eliot. *Matthew Calbraith Perry.* Boston and New York: Houghton, Mifflin & Co., 1890.

Huntington, W. P. *Perry's Victory Memorial.* Akron, O.: The Commercial Printing & Lithographing Co., 1917.

Jarvis, Russel. *A Biographical Notice of Commander Jesse D. Elliott (containing a review of the controversy between him and the late Commodore Perry.) . . . By a citizen of New York.* Printed for the Author, Philadelphia, 1835.

Judson, Isaac R. *General William H. Harrison, with a sketch of the Life of William Henry Harrison attributed to Isaac R. Judson.* Philadelphia: J. Harding, 1840.

Long, Laura. *Oliver Hazard Perry.* Indianapolis: The Bobbs-Merrill Co., 1949.

Lossing, Benson J. *The Pictorial Field Book of the War of 1812.* New York: Harper & Bros., 1869.

Lyman, Olin Linus. *Commodore Oliver Hazard Perry and the Battle of Lake Erie.* New York: New Amsterdam Book Co., 1905.

Mackenzie, Alex. Slidell. *Commodore Oliver Hazard Perry.* Akron, O.: J. K. Richardson & Sons, 1910.

————. *The Life of Commodore Oliver Hazard Perry.* New York: Harper & Bros., 1840.

Mills, James Cooke. *Oliver Hazard Perry and the Battle of Lake Erie.* Detroit: J. Phelps, 1913.

Niles, John Milton. *The Life of Oliver Hazard Perry.* Hartford, Conn.: U. S. Marsh, 1820.

Niles, William O. *Tippecanoe Text Book.* Baltimore: D. Green, 1840.

Parsons, Usher. *Battle of Lake Erie.* Providence, R. I.: B. T. Albro, Ptrs., 1854.

Paullin, Chas. O. *The Battle of Lake Erie.* Cleveland: The Rowfant Club, 1918.

Perry, Rev. Calbraith B. *The Perrys of Rhode Island and Tales of Silver Creek.* New York: Tobias A. Wright, 1913.

Rosenberg, Max. *The Building of Perry's Fleet on Lake Erie.* The Commonwealth of Pennsylvania: Printers for the Pennsylvania Historical Commission, 1950.

Snider, C. H. J. *In the Wake of the Eighteentwelvers.* London and New York: John Lane Co., 1913.

Spalding, Rufus Paine. *Oration of the Honorable Rufus P. Spalding with an account of the Celebration of the Anniversary of The Battle of Lake Erie and Laying the Cornerstone of the Monument—Sept. 10, 1859.* Sandusky, Ohio: H. D. Cooke & Co., 1859.

Todd, Col. C. S. *Sketches of the Civil and Military Services of William Henry Harrison.* Cincinnati: J. A. & W. P. James, 1847.

Tucker, Glenn. *Poltroons and Patriots.* Indianapolis: The Bobbs-Merrill Co., 1954.

Walker, Adam. *A Journal of the U. S. Fourth Infantry (1811-1812).* Keene, N. H.: Sentinel Press, 1816.

Transcript of the Trial of Robert Barclay at the Court Martial held aboard His Majesty's Ship "Gladiator" at Portsmouth Harbor, September 9, 1814.
Bureau of Navigation Records.
Navy Registers, 1814-1820.
Nominations for Appointment etc., 1798-1820.
Letters to Officers—Ships of War Nos. 1-5, 8-13.
Letter Book, May 1799 to July 1807.
Private Letters, February 1813 to January 1840.
Captains' Letters, Vol. 6, p. 168, 1813.
———, Vol. 7, p. 2, 1813.
———, Vol. 8, p. 29, 1813.
———, Vol. 1, p. 131, 1814.
———, Vol. 4, pp. 44, 48, 1816.
———, Vol. 1, pp. 11, 62, 63, 1817.
———, Vol. 2, pp. 118, 119, 1817.
———, Vol. 4, p. 88, 1817.
Miscellaneous material, May 26, 1813, Accession 2258.
Personal papers of B. W. Crowninshield.
Papers of Oliver Hazard Perry, Accession 1015.
Papers of Charles Chauncey, Accession 3375.
Master Commandants' Letters, 1812, 1813.
All above material in Office of Naval Records in Archives Building, Washington, D. C., and in Navy Library, Constitution Ave., Washington, D. C., and in Bureau of Navigation, Washington, D. C.

NEWSPAPERS AND PERIODICALS

Annals of Congress, Vols. 31 & 32, 1817-1818, at 1st Session of the 15th Congress.
American State Papers—Naval Affairs.
Vol. 1, pp. 470-480 (1834).
Vol. 1, pp. 453, 457. (1818).
Niles Register, May 14, 1814, pp. 125.
January 8, 1814, pp. 14-15.

March 11, 1815, pp. 29, 30.

August 24, 1816, pp. 424, 425, 426, 427.

February 17, 1816, pp. 428, 429.

July 5, 1817, pp. 292, 293.

October 13, 1818, pp. 152, 153.

March 7, 1818, pp. 29, 30, 31.

October 24, 1818, p. 140.

Ontario Historical Society Papers and Records, Vol. 14, Chapter 5, pp. 169-178.

New York Genealogical and Biographical Record. Published by the New York Genealogical and Historical Society. N.Y., January 1937. Vol. 68, pp. 1, 2, 181, 157, 289.

National Cyclopaedia and American Biography. James T. White & Co., 1892. Vol. 7, p. 39. Vol. 13, p. 35.

Pennsylvania Magazine of History and Biography. Published by the Pennsylvania Historical Society, Philadelphia. Vol. 74, pp. 113-141. Article, "Diplomacy in Barbary" by Roy F. Nichols.

Ohio Historical and Philosophical Society, Bulletin of. Published by the Society in Cincinnati, Ohio. Vol. 9, pp. 282, 318.

Michigan History. Published by Michigan Historical Commission. Vol. 40, p. 438.

Newport Historical Society. "Items of Interest regarding Oliver Hazard Perry, in Newport and Newport in the War of 1812." Newport, R.I.: Mercury Publishing Co., 1913.

Report of The Perry's Victory Centennial Commission of the State of New York. Compiled by George D. Emerson, Sec'y. Published by J. B. Lyons Co., Albany, N.Y., 1916.

Serious Charges against Captain Oliver Hazard Perry of the United States Navy, by John Heath, Late Captain of the Marine Corps. Published Washington, D.C., June 15, 1817. Provided by the John Carter Brown Library, Providence, R. I.

Analectic Magazine, December 1813, Vol. 2, pp. 494-510.

Cleveland Plain Dealer, September 8, 1838 and November 15, 1940 (1940).

Western Reserve and Northern Ohio Historical Society Tract No. 36. Cleveland, Ohio, 1877. Memorandum and Notes on William Henry Harrison, by A. T. Goodman.